Primary Initiatives in Mathematics Education

CALCULATORS, CHILDREN AND MATHEMATICS

Hilary Shuard

Angela Walsh

Jeffrey Goodwin

Valerie Worcester

SIMON & S

LONDON • SYDNEY • NEW YORK • TO

The Primary Initiatives in Mathematics Education Project
was launched by the School Curriculum Development
Committee in September 1985 and completed under
the auspices of the National Curriculum Council in
August 1989.

National Curriculum Council
Albion Wharf
25 Skeldergate
York YO1 2XL

First published in 1991 in Great Britain by
Simon & Schuster Ltd
Wolsey House
Wolsey Road
Hemel Hempstead HP2 4SS

Printed in Great Britain by
St Edmundsbury Press
Bury St Edmunds

British Cataloguing in Publication Data

Calculators, children and mathematics
    1. Schools. Curriculum subjects mathematics
    I. Shuard, Hilary   II. Series
    510.78

Edited by John Day
Designed by Danuta Trebus and Jerry Watkiss
Artwork by Jerry Watkiss/Kingsway Advertising

CONTENTS

PREFACE

The PrIME project (Primary Initiatives in Mathematics Education) was a curriculum development project in primary mathematics. It was funded from 1985 to 1989, at first by the School Curriculum Development Committee (SCDC), and then by the National Curriculum Council (NCC), which took over the existing curriculum development work of the SCDC in 1988. The central project team consisted of four members and an administrator, and was based at Homerton College, Cambridge. The project team are most grateful to the Principal, staff and students for the friendly welcome that the college gave them, and for the College's unstinting support. Thanks are also due to the professional staff of SCDC and NCC, especially Gordon Turner (SCDC) and Chris Jones (NCC), who ably and enthusiastically supported the project.

This book is an account of work which the PrIME Project undertook, between 1986 and 1989, to develop a Calculator-Aware Number (CAN) curriculum for children in the primary years. The work is continuing until 1992, under the auspices of the CAN Continuation Project, but the account in this book only goes up to 1989, when the oldest children were aged nine. Many teachers have worked on CAN to produce the work described in this book. It is their book – the PrIME Project team has only put it together on their behalf. The book is supported by a 27-minute videotape shot in classrooms. This is also entitled *Calculators, Children and Mathematics*, and is published by Simon and Schuster.

It is hoped that the book will reach some readers outside Britain. To assist their understanding, some details of the British educational scene are desribed in greater detail than would be necessary if the readership were drawn entirely from Britain. We hope that British readers will forgive what may seem to them to be excessive details.

Other aspects of the work of the PrIME project culminated in the production of a pack of INSET activities for groups of primary teachers, intended to assist them in reflecting on and developing their practice in the teaching of mathematics. The pack is entitled *Children, Mathematics and Learning*, and is published by Simon and Schuster (1990). It contains sections on problem solving and investigation, using calculators and computers, doing and talking mathematics, a cross-curricular approach, managing mathematics learning, children as learners of mathematics, mathematics for all, and involving parents in mathematics.

Hilary Shuard
Angela Walsh
Jeffrey Goodwin
Valerie Worcester

December 1990

Revision of the National Curriculum in Mathematics

The structure of the Attainment Targets in mathematics is to be simplified. At the time of going to press (February 1991), it is understood that this will be achieved without altering the existing content of the Curriculum. The number of Levels of Attainment will also, of course, remain unaltered. Therefore, the place of the CAN curriculum in the National Curriculum, as described in this book, will be **unaffected**.

Because of the pressing demand for information on the CAN curriculum, it was decided not to delay publication until after the completion of the revision.

THE NEW TECHNOLOGY OF CALCULATION

1

The availability of calculators

This book describes a curriculum development project in England and Wales, in the period 1986–9, the aim of which was to study effects that the availability of calculators would have on the mathematics curriculum of primary schools. Thus, it was intended to develop a calculator-aware mathematics curriculum, especially in number, for children in the primary (five to 11) age range. The project team hopes that this account of their work will help teachers in primary schools to understand how much calculators have to offer young children; the team also hopes that teachers will grasp opportunities for using calculators to help children to understand numbers and to use numbers with enjoyment and knowledge.

By 1985, when the project started, simple electronic calculators had become common-place tools, which were in everyday use by many adults in Britain. Calculators are cheap and portable, and they take the labour out of calculation. Many people now own a calculator; indeed, the sales of calculators in Britain have reached six million a year, so that about one person in ten buys a new calculator each year.

During the mid-1980s, several investigations were undertaken to find out how much adults used calculators at work, and to find out whether children had access to calculators at home. In surveying the use of calculators by adults at work in 1985, Fitzgerald (1985) found that:

> *When employees still have to perform calculations, use of the electronic calculator is almost ubiquitous. It has become very rare indeed to find an employee performing multiplication, division or percentage calculations, except sometimes the simpler kinds, using written methods.*

At work, the most important need in calculation is to get the correct answer, and to get it as quickly as possible. Hence, people use calculators whenever it is quicker, easier and more accurate to do so.

Children, too, value correct answers to calculations, but they are often required at school to use non-calculator methods of calculation. However, they may have calculators at home, even if they are not allowed to use them at school. In early 1984, Shuard surveyed 500 children aged seven to 11 in and around Cambridge (Shuard and Smith 1985), and found the results shown below. At that time,

	Girls (%)	Boys (%)
Child has own calculator	49	62
Famliy member has a calculator	86	87

it was a surprise that so many children had access to calculators.

In 1985, Anita Straker undertook a wider-ranging survey of about 2000 top infants and 2000 third-year juniors in different parts of England (Straker 1985). Her figures were slightly lower than those found in 'high-tech' Cambridge, but, in her survey, more than a third of top infant boys (aged six to seven), and more than half of third-year junior boys (aged nine to ten), had a calculator of their own. The figures for calculator ownership among girls were somewhat smaller. Overall, in this survey, about 70% of children lived in families where a family member had a calculator. Thus, by the mid-1980s, the majority of primary children probably had access to a calculator owned by a member of their family, and a surprising number of children had a calculator of their own, even at the age of six.

Calculator use in school

The Cockcroft Report (DES 1982) made several statements about the role of calculators in the primary classroom. This important national report was written at a time when calculators were first becoming everyday tools for adults, but when they were not yet widely used in schools. The Report stated:

> *There is as yet little evidence about the extent to which a calculator should be used instead of pencil and paper for purposes of calculation in the primary years; nor is there evidence about the eventual balance to be obtained at the primary stage between calculations carried out mentally, on paper, or with a calculator. However, it is clear that the arithmetical aspects of the primary curriculum cannot but be affected by the increasing availability of calculators.*
>
> [Para 387]

In 1985, it was very clear that the arithmetical aspects of the primary curriculum had still not been affected by calculators. By this time, documents which encouraged the use of calculators in schools had been produced by some LEAs, and by groups such as the Open University (1982) and the Mathematical Association (1985). However, these documents seem to have had little effect on practice in primary schools. Calculators were still not available in the majority of primary schools, and children were not usually allowed to bring their own calculators from home. Some schools seemed to regard calculator use as 'cheating'. Commercial publications provided little support for the use of calculators in mathematics, and they did not encourage teachers to use them with their classes. The number work in the published mathematics schemes which most primary schools used was still based on the traditional vertical pencil-and-paper methods of carrying out addition, subtraction, multiplication and division; these methods have been taught with little change throughout this century. The published schemes either provided a few calculator activities as optional extras, or they ignored calculators altogether.

The Cockcroft Report spelled out the fact that there was an urgent need for the investigation and development of calculator use in primary schools:

Some development work on the use of calculators in the primary years is going on at the present time. In our view, more is needed both to consider the use of calculators as an aid to teaching and learning within the primary mathematics curriculum as a whole and also the extent to which the arithmetical aspects of the curriculum may need to be modified. [Para 388]

In 1985 the time was ripe for a substantial investigation into the effects which an acceptance of calculators into the primary classroom would have. The nationally-funded curriculum development project PrIME (Primary Initiatives in Mathematics Education) provided an opportunity for that exploration. The project was based in England and Wales, and this book describes only the calculator work of the PrIME project. However, a search of the literature shows that very little similar work on calculator use in the primary years was being carried out anywhere else in the world. The primary mathematics curriculum everywhere was still based on the old technology of pencil-and-paper calculation.

SETTING UP THE CAN PROJECT | 2

The PrIME project

The PrIME project (Primary Initiatives in Mathematics Education) was a nationally-funded curriculum development project in primary mathematics which operated in England and Wales from 1985 to 1989; it was funded first by the School Curriculum Development Committee and then by the National Curriculum Council.

The main aims of the PrIME project are listed below. The emphasised section shows the aim of PrIME's calculator work.

■ To enable teachers to develop their thinking and understanding about primary mathematics and its learning and teaching.

■ To encourage teachers to make use of all the teaching styles listed in paragraph 243 of the Cockcroft Report.

■ *To develop the primary mathematics curriculum to take full account of the impact of new technology, concentrating especially on the importance of calculators for the number curriculum,* and on computer-based environments such as LOGO for the development of children's mathematical thinking.

To carry out the calculator-related aim, the project set up groups of teachers to investigate the effect of the complete acceptance of calculators in the primary classroom over a long period of time; during this investigation, a calculator-aware number (CAN) curriculum emerged.

To work on its other aims, PrIME established, in various LEAs, groups of primary teachers who worked together to develop their own mathematics teaching, to develop their curriculum, and to devise INSET materials (Shuard *et al* 1990). A style of working emerged which depended on mutual support and the sharing of ideas within a group; this style was also very apparent in the groups of teachers who worked in CAN.

Although CAN was part of the PrIME project, this book does not consist of INSET activities, as do the other PrIME materials. It is more appropriate to a continuing long-term development such as CAN that the book should give an account of the changes that took place in the children, in the teaching and in the curriculum.

In reading this account, the reader needs to appreciate that although CAN became very important to all who were involved, it was planned as only a small part of the PrIME project's work. The financial contribution which PrIME could make to CAN was small, and much of the funding came from the participating LEAs, because of the goodwill and support of their mathematics advisers. The participating teachers also sustained the work by their enthusiasm, their commitment and their willingness to respond to new needs and to develop new ideas.

The philosophy of CAN

Before any schools were recruited, the PrIME project team discussed and clarified their own ideas about CAN. The major principle was that:

> *Children should be allowed to use calculators in the same way that adults use them: at their own choice, whenever they wish to do so.*

This principle was developed so that a discussion document could be written for the first group of project teachers. The discussion document put forward general guidelines, as far as these could be predicted when there was no similar experience of free use of calculators by young children. However, much other experience of good primary practice in mathematics could be applied to CAN. The following ideas emerged:

■ Children should always have a calculator available. The choice as to whether to use a calculator or some other method of calculation was to be the children's, not the teacher's.

■ The traditional vertical pencil-and-paper methods for addition, subtraction, multiplication and division would not be taught. They would not be needed, because children could always use calculators for calculations which they could not do mentally.

■ CAN would be based on 'good primary practice'; it would be practical and investigational, with much emphasis on language activities and work across the whole curriculum. It was hoped that children would find it enjoyable and interesting.

■ Exploring and investigating 'how numbers work' would be encouraged. Use of apparatus and practical materials would continue. Many activities would not be directly associated with calculators, but would be intended to help children's understanding of number.

■ It was important for children's understanding of number that they should develop their mathematical language and their confidence in talking about numbers.

■ The importance of mental calculation would be emphasised. Children would be encouraged to share their methods of mental calculation with others.

■ Number work would occupy less than half of the mathematics time. It was hoped that changing only the curriculum in 'number' would limit to manageable proportions the amount of rethinking that project teachers would need to do.

It was clear from these starting points that, once a group of children had started on CAN, it would not be easy for them to abandon it. The children's experience of number, and of mathematics in general, would be very different from that of their contemporaries who did not use calculators, and who learnt the traditional vertical pencil-and-paper methods of calculation. It was hoped that the children would be more accustomed to exploration and investigation in mathematics, and to talking about the mathematics they were doing. If they gave up CAN, they would probably not move back very easily into the style of mathematics found in the published mathematics schemes available at the time.

However, the use of calculators seemed to be becoming more common in secondary schools, and changes to more investigational methods in GCSE were being proposed. It seemed unlikely, as far as could be predicted in 1985, that disaster would befall the children if they had to move into a fairly conventional secondary school mathematics programme in six or seven years time.

These considerations led the project team to consider recruiting schools where groups of children would be able to work on CAN throughout the whole of their primary education. However, this was not practicable, as it would require at least a seven-year programme, and PrIME was only funded until 1989. The compromise was finally reached that CAN would be started with groups of top infants (aged six to seven) in September 1986. These were thought to be the oldest children who would not already have been exposed to a very substantial diet of traditional pencil-and-paper methods of calculation. In 1989 they would be aged nine, and it was hoped that it would be possible to continue to support them in CAN until they were aged 11.

The project LEAs

In late 1985, the PrIME project wrote to all LEAs in England and Wales to explain the proposed work on the CAN curriculum, and to invite LEAs to apply for the involvement of some of their schools. Attention was drawn to the long-term nature of the project:

> *It is hoped that the project will be able to identify a few LEAs and schools which are willing to engage in developing and trialling the project's 'calculator-aware number curriculum', over a period of years from top infant level upwards towards the later primary years.*

LEAs were told that the predominant methods of calculation used would be 'in the head' and 'with a calculator', and that the traditional vertical pencil-and-paper methods of calculation would not be taught. Because of these

major changes from the traditional content of primary number work, consultation with all concerned was urged:

> *The development of this curriculum area will need to call on a great deal of enthusiasm and commitment from the schools and teachers involved. The children's parents and the receiving secondary school will need to be consulted and involved. … It is hoped that the first groups of top infants will be able to work on a pilot programme in September 1986. A second cohort of top infants will embark on the programme (in a revised form) in September 1987.*

After much consultation, four LEAs in England took part in CAN: Doncaster, a consortium drawn from Durham and Newcastle upon Tyne, and Suffolk. In Wales, Dyfed joined CAN; it was first funded by SCDC Wales, and then by the Curriculum Committee for Wales. The initial work in Dyfed was in Welsh-medium schools, although some English-medium schools joined the project later. In all cases, LEAs made their own choice of the schools to be involved.

Four other LEAs affiliated and worked on CAN under their own initiative, without any financial support from the project. These were Havering, Lancashire, Rochdale, and the Inner London Education Authority. (On the closure of ILEA, the project schools in London came under the new Tower Hamlets LEA.)

The project schools and classes

CAN started in 1986 with children aged six in about 20 classes in some 15 schools. The schools represented a mixture of large and small schools in urban, country and suburban environments; however, inner-city schools were under-represented. The numbers of classes and schools fluctuated somewhat; although most children were in single-age classes, some were in vertically grouped classes, and some of these children moved to new classes at different times of the year.

Most types of school organisation were to be found: five-to-eleven primary schools, separate infant (five-to-seven) and junior (seven-to-eleven) schools, five-to-eight and five-to-nine first schools and their corresponding eight-to-twelve and nine-to-thirteen middle schools. In this variety of structures, some children moved to a new school at the end of each year of the project.

Schools were only requested to take two year-groups of children into the CAN project; they could then revert to traditional methods for later year-groups. However, this has not happened; in all the schools, all later year-groups have joined the project, so that CAN is becoming a whole-school enterprise.

All the schools agreed that, if all went well, the oldest children would continue to work on CAN until they were aged 11. In situations where the age of transfer to the next school was not 11, this meant that the receiving junior or middle school also had to join the project.

Considerable liaison between schools was necessary in order to ensure continuity and the continuance of a CAN style of teaching.

Because of the need to keep parents informed about the changes, LEAs were asked to select schools which had good relations with parents, and the confidence of their governing bodies. In many ways, the project schools were representative of schools everywhere, although some of them had an unusually strong abiding interest in children's mathematical development. It was essential that the headteacher should be committed to the project, but in some schools not all the teachers were initially committed. CAN was introduced to each class as project children arrived in it, so not all the teachers were involved at the start of the project.

Some schools have now decided to develop the CAN philosophy from reception classes upwards. As the headteacher of one school wrote:

The spreading of the CAN philosophy in school has been rapidly accelerated by the movement of an experienced teacher who was involved in the first year of CAN with a class of six and seven-year-olds, to a reception class of four and five-year-olds. This teacher has used the methods, and many of the activities and ideas that she developed with her six and seven-year-olds, with great success. This approach has spread sideways, as the two other reception teachers have seen how the children have developed mathematically.

Although the PrIME project finished in 1989, the project schools have all continued to work on CAN, under the auspices of the CAN Continuation Project. At the time of writing, the oldest children in the project are aged ten to 11, and are in the fourth junior year. All the original Partner and Affiliated LEAs are involved in the CAN Continuation Project; not only are the original schools still involved, but in all these LEAs, some other schools have joined the project.

Support for project schools

Each LEA appointed a local coordinator, who was usually an advisory teacher; the project's funding provided one-fifth of the salary of the coordinator, who could thus spend one day a week on CAN. In practice, LEAs allowed coordinators to spend much more time than this in supporting CAN. LEAs also contributed funding to support the release of teachers to attend local and national project meetings.

Regular local teachers' meetings in each LEA were an important feature of the project. At these meetings classroom activities were invented and shared, common problems were discussed, and the meetings also gave teachers the opportunity to work together in a CAN environment. Annual conferences for participating teachers enabled them to meet teachers from other LEAs, to discuss future directions which the work might take, and to learn from the different approaches and styles which each LEA brought to the project.

The project would not have been able to work on such a large scale if it had not been for the support of the calculator manufacturing company Texas Instruments. This firm gave a four-function calculator for every child who took part in the project – a total of 800 in the first year of CAN. Texas Instruments generously kept up this level of support throughout the lifetime of CAN, so that every child in CAN in Partner LEAs has had access to a calculator whenever it was needed. The TI–1103 calculators provided were sturdy, hard-wearing and suitable for young children.

Styles of classroom work

In many of the project schools, published mathematics schemes had previously been in use. Most of the number work in these schemes was geared towards developing and practising the traditional pencil-and-paper vertical methods of calculation. Schools were therefore asked not to use the number work in published schemes, although there was no objection to the use of schemes in other areas of mathematics such as measures and shape and space. It was also thought that teachers who were accustomed to a published scheme would find the project too difficult if all published materials were discouraged. Some schools cut up textbooks and made workcards from the pages they would continue to use, others withdrew some workcards from their scheme. In general, over the years, the project teachers have moved away from published schemes as they have become more self-confident in their thinking.

Omitting the teaching of the traditional vertical pencil-and-paper methods of calculation has released a great deal of time to promote children's understanding of number, and this has been an important factor in the development of children's ability to think mathematically. In fact, the CAN philosophy has proved to be much more than just using a calculator. It quickly became apparent that children did not always choose to use a calculator; 'doing it yourself' without the calculator became an attractive and challenging option to many children, as did problem-solving and investigational work. One headteacher wrote about the project:

Perhaps the word 'calculator' in the title has been given too much emphasis; initially both parents and visiting staff seemed to expect to see children using calculators for all their calculations and were agreeably surprised to note that this is not the case.

The teaching style which has developed has given the children autonomy in their learning, allowing them to find their own ways of tackling problems, and their own mental and non-calculator methods of calculation. The teachers have been very resourceful in devising activities, and in encouraging a problem-solving and investigational approach which does not constrain the children. For some teachers this approach was not new:

> **Yes, it fits in comfortably with what I was doing before. I don't think it's changed much.**

> **Not radically different from what we were doing before.**

For other teachers it was a radical change:

> **It has changed my way of teaching maths, even in such a short time. I look at things differently. The CAN approach is very different from what I've done before.**

A CAN style of working has also gradually taken over in other areas of work in many classrooms. A headteacher wrote:

> **The project has developed during its lifetime. From the initial concept of a calculator-based curriculum within the 'number' aspect of mathematics it has broadened, first into all the other areas of mathematics and then beyond mathematics itself.**

Yet the calculator does play an important part in the project. It allows children to handle large numbers, beyond those that they could work with mentally or with pencil and paper. Children are able to use 'real life' numbers in 'real life' situations; there is no longer a need to simplify numbers and situations. Children explore and play not only with large numbers, but also with decimals and negative numbers, and in doing so, they gradually understand the structure of numbers. The calculator gives children scope to explore, and each situation is capable of generating further situations for children to explore. And the children constantly surprise their teachers; as one teacher wrote:

> **I'm constantly amazed at how much further on they are compared with following a traditional scheme. Previously I would never have found out what children can really do, about their understanding of large numbers.**

Getting started

Different schools and different teachers started to work on CAN in different ways. The headteacher of one school has described in detail how it started there:

> **Before the work began there were a couple of terms of thinking and discussion within the school and with the project team. We had been using calculators with children for four or five years, and my feeling was that it would be an extension of what we were doing already. That turned out to be quite wrong.**

The teachers at this school decided that they would not 'instruct' the children in the use of the calculator, but that they would always answer direct questions from the children. At first, nothing much seemed to be happening:

> **Normal good practice was continuing as we had agreed that it should, and non-number aspects of maths were unchanged. The children were obviously very attracted by the bright red and blue calculators with their slide-on covers. They loved having their very own machine, and they proudly carried them about everywhere, sitting them on the table even when they were reading or writing a story. It was noticeable that the calculators showed up in a lot of their paintings at this time.**

The class teacher made use of this interest, suggesting that children should make junk model calculators. She encouraged the children to look closely at the way the numbers were arranged on the keypad, so that they could get their models right. They also made number-lines with matchsticks on black sugar paper, using the digital number shapes.

Gradually the calculator began to be used in number work, but not in the way the teachers had expected. The head continued:

> **I recall watching one child with a large piece of paper, some Multilink cubes and a calculator. The paper was blank but the calculator displayed 7714. I was not immediately able to relate the child's actions, pushing cubes backwards and forwards and counting them, to the number on the display. So I asked her what she was doing. 'I'm making 14, all different ways.' 'And does this help?' I asked, picking up the calculator. 'Oh yes, it helps you to remember what you are doing – look, it says 7 and 7 make 14.'**

For some time the children used the calculator as an electronic notebook, to remind them of the numbers they were using. Gradually they found out, and showed each other, that you could use the calculator to give you the answer to sums you hadn't worked out for yourself. A child said to the head:

> 'Look! Five add one makes ... six, right? [Doing it.] But you can put in FIVE HUNDRED add one! See! What number is that?'

> 'It's 501, and that's how you write it.'

> 'Wow!'

The class teacher became very enthusiastic about the children's conversations, and felt that their thinking was developing rapidly. Later in the year, the head overheard two children arguing about the number displayed on a calculator.

> 'It says ten thousand.'

> 'No, it's a hundred thousand.'

'TEN thousand. Look – divide by two. What do you get?'

'Oh ... five thousand. You're right.'

The headteacher continued to reflect:

> **I started to realise that, far from being a continuation of our previous work, CAN was a direct challenge to it, forcing some difficult and uncomfortable questions upon us.**

The teachers at this school had not previously questioned the good primary practice that they were trying to carry out. The head listed some aspects of their good primary practice:

- Proceed from the known to the unknown.
- Make everything concrete.
- Don't force abstraction on children at an early stage.

But the children in the project were forcing their teachers to reconsider these beliefs:

> **These children seemed to be overleaping the need for apparatus, using it only to demonstrate or explain their thinking. They went determinedly in abstract directions, experimenting with all the buttons on all the numbers they could think of. We didn't have millions of Multilink cubes, and the children wouldn't have bothered with them if we had.**
>
> **We recognised that a lot of the power that was being generated was because the children had a large measure of control over the content of what they did.**

3 CHILDREN'S CONCEPTS OF NUMBER

The use of calculators

From the beginning of the project, children were allowed free access to calculators alongside other apparatus. A report from one LEA, after three years of work, describes the significance of this:

> *A significant finding from the project is that calculators should be viewed as an item of multi-purpose mathematical apparatus and that teachers do not need to design specific tasks to bring them into play. Pupils select the calculator as they feel it is appropriate to the task in hand just as they would select other material – Multilink, counters, modelling apparatus etc. to solve the problem they are dealing with.*
>
> [Durham County Council 1989]

However, the frequent use of calculators has made the mathematical experience of project children different from the experience of other children. Many children have developed mathematical concepts and methods which have not in the past been expected at their age. For young children, the calculator is a toy, but it is the first toy for young children that incorporates the number system. As children play with their calculators, they find out a great deal about how numbers behave.

Ready access to calculators has also given the children great confidence. They are never faced with calculations that they cannot do. Their problem now is to decide the appropriate calculation to do in order to solve a problem, and to interpret the results of that calculation in the problem situation. Exploration and investigation have taken over from the repetitive practice of calculation as the usual style of number work.

This chapter gives an account, with examples, of work on number done by project children aged six to nine. The extracts are chosen to show their developing understanding of number concepts. In many cases their teachers were also exploring CAN for the first time, and they were often surprised by what the children did.

Most children in the project have also decided for themselves that they do not need, or want, to be dependent on their calculators for all calculation. It is often faster and easier to do a calculation mentally, and children sometimes vie with one another to extend their skill in mental calculation. The project has seen a great flowering of mental calculation, often led by the children. Chapter 4 (pages 24-34) gives examples of their mental and other non-calculator methods of calculation.

Place value

When young children first start to work on CAN, the following activity, invented by a teacher, is a popular one: Put a number inside a square. Then put a number at each corner of the square so that the four 'corner' numbers add up to the number in the square.

Gary's way of doing this (Figure 3.1) was a surprise to his teacher, who had not yet 'done' any work with these six-year-old children on place value in hundreds. However, Gary seemed to have found out how to decompose a three-digit number into hundreds, tens and units, although he was not yet sure which way round to write 7.

Figure 3.1

At the same time, in the same class, Sara was experimenting with seven and eight-digit numbers. She was also varying the activity, using triangles with three numbers (Figure 3.2).

In another class, two children were throwing dice and entering the numbers shown on prepared two-digit grids, to make a biggest number or a smallest number. One said: 'I like getting smallest numbers best because then you have to put small numbers at the front.'

A teacher described a six-year-old's work on the following activity: How much water do we drink at lunch time (the whole class or school)?

▉ I chatted to each group, and asked them to explain how they had worked it out. One girl seemed to be in difficulties. She had on her paper:

10 glasses was 1200 millilitres

so I asked her how much 20 glasses would be. It was quite a time before she said: 'Two of those,' and wrote:

20 glasses was 2400 millilitres

I asked how much 30 glasses would be. After what seemed like eternity, when she was working on another task, she wrote:

30 was 3600 ml

I was really pleased when having read out the number as 'three hundred and sixty millilitres' she then said: 'No, it's three thousand six hundred.' ◗

Another teacher asked Carole (aged eight) what the number after 2799 was. Carole answered orally: 'Two thousand eight hundred,' but when asked to show it on her calculator said that she couldn't. 'Can you show me two thousand on the calculator?' Carole did. 'Can you show me two thousand and three on the calculator?' Carole then continued successfully to show numbers up to 2009. 'What is the next number, Carole?' Carole answered: 'Two thousand and ten,' but showed it on the calculator as 200010. The teacher then showed Carole that 2000 plus 6 entered on the calculator gave 2006, and 2000 plus 13 gave 2013 on the calculator. She did 2000 plus 17 correctly and correctly entered several similar addition statements. She was then asked to write 2039 on the calculator, and did this correctly by entering the number directly, not by addition.

For many children, the correct way of writing numbers in the thousands is not at first obvious. Peter started with a four-spike abacus, and arranged two beads as shown in Figure 3.3. He said: 'It's one thousand one hundred. How do you write it down?' The teacher asked him what he thought, and Peter said: 'I know – I'll use the calculator.' He keyed in:

Figure 3.3

$$1000 + 100 =$$

and the display showed the information he needed.

These examples show that many children who use calculators find place value in hundreds and thousands difficult at first, as do their contemporaries who do not use calculators. However, the calculator gives an additional way of exploring place value, by adding known numbers on the calculator, as Carole and Peter did.

Large numbers

Most children enjoy using the largest numbers they can handle confidently. Many CAN activities encourage children to use numbers of their own choice, allowing the more able children to extend their command of numbers, while the less able remain within the limits of their competence. Both the children whose work is shown in Figures 3.4a, b, were aged seven and both were regarded as 'slow learners'. They were 'making 19'. Steve was much more confident than Stewart, but eventually the numbers grew beyond his control.

It is very common for children working in CAN to make patterns such as these, and many children seem to be fascinated by number patterns. The calculator makes it easy for a pattern to be extended as far as a child wishes, so that the regularity of the pattern can be observed and the next number predicted. However, children often do not use the calculator when they are generating a pattern; indeed, the mistakes in the second half of Steve's work suggest that he did not even verify his pattern on the calculator. Steve and Stewart's patterns were rather short in length. Some schools found it a problem that children continued the same pattern for many pages. The teachers tried to persuade children that, once the pattern had been established and verified, there was no point in going on with the same pattern for ever.

Because children who use calculators are able to handle large numbers, they can work in real-life situations in which the numbers have not been simplified. Kelly and

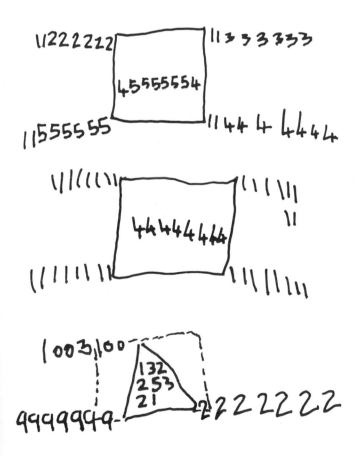

Figure 3.2

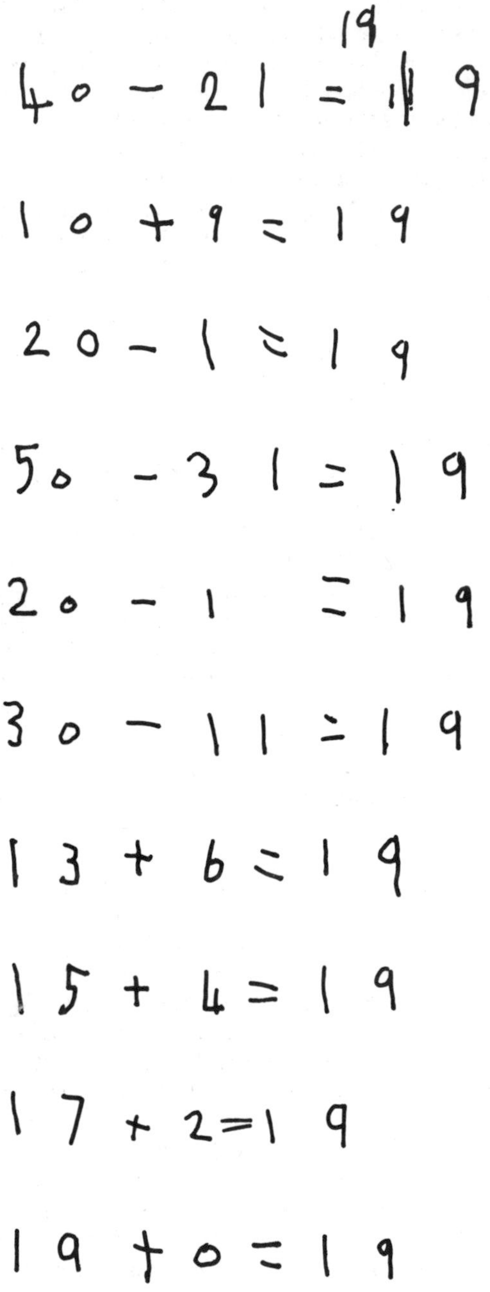

$$40 - 21 = \overset{19}{1}\, 9$$

$$10 + 9 = 1\,9$$

$$20 - 1 = 1\,9$$

$$50 - 31 = 1\,9$$

$$20 - 1 = 1\,9$$

$$30 - 11 = 1\,9$$

$$13 + 6 = 1\,9$$

$$15 + 4 = 1\,9$$

$$17 + 2 = 1\,9$$

$$19 + 0 = 1\,9$$

Figure 3.4a Stewart's work

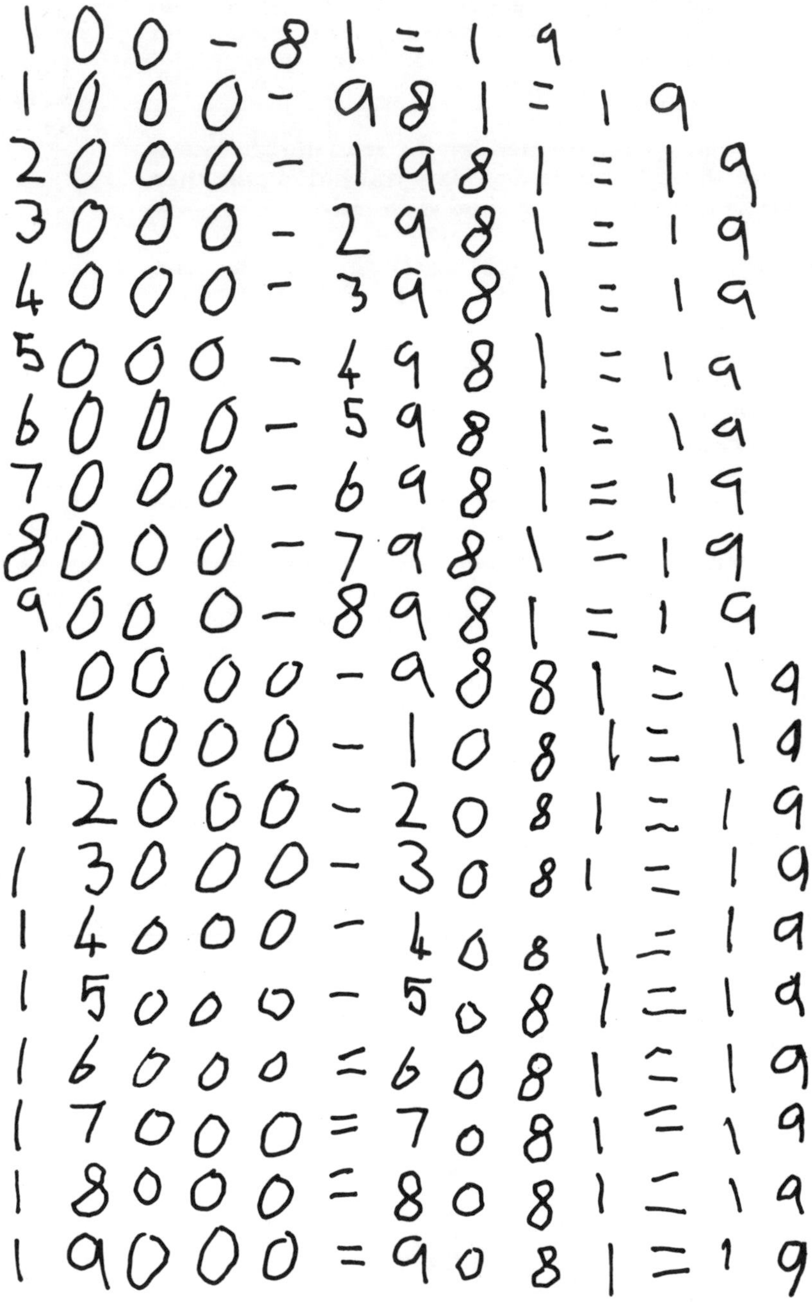

$$100 - 81 = 1\,9$$

$$1000 - 981 = 1\,9$$

$$2000 - 1981 = 1\,9$$

$$3000 - 2981 = 1\,9$$

$$4000 - 3981 = 1\,9$$

$$5000 - 4981 = 1\,9$$

$$6000 - 5981 = 1\,9$$

$$7000 - 6981 = 1\,9$$

$$8000 - 7981 = 1\,9$$

$$9000 - 8981 = 1\,9$$

$$10000 - 9881 = 1\,9$$

$$11000 - 1081 = 1\,9$$

$$12000 - 2081 = 1\,9$$

$$13000 - 3081 = 1\,9$$

$$14000 - 4081 = 1\,9$$

$$15000 - 5081 = 1\,9$$

$$16000 = 6081 = 1\,9$$

$$17000 = 7081 = 1\,9$$

$$18000 = 8081 = 1\,9$$

$$19000 = 9081 = 1\,9$$

Figure 3.4b Steve's work

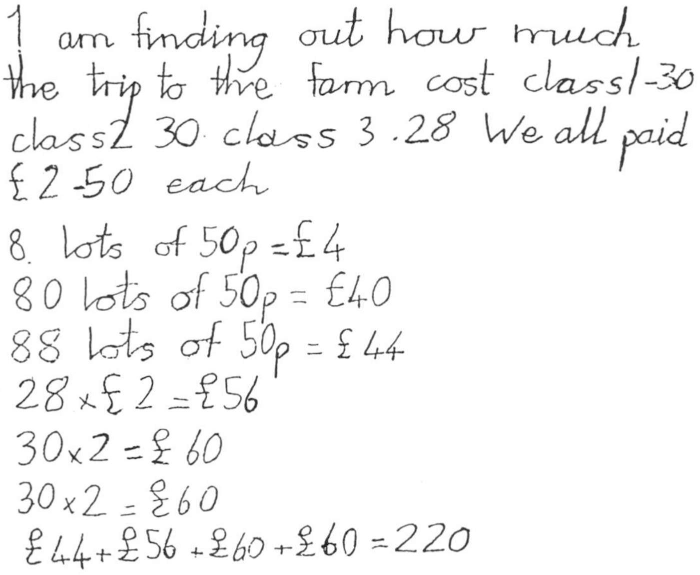

I am finding out how much the trip to the farm cost class1-30 class2 30 class 3 .28 We all paid £2-50 each

8 lots of 50p = £4
80 lots of 50p = £40
88 lots of 50p = £44
28 × £2 = £56
30 × 2 = £60
30 × 2 = £60
£44 + £56 + £60 + £60 = 220

Figure 3.5a Kelly's method

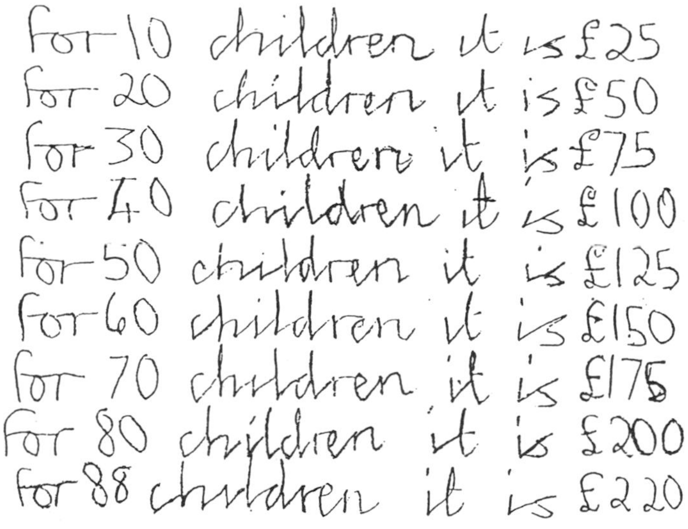

For 10 children it is £25
For 20 children it is £50
For 30 children it is £75
For 40 children it is £100
For 50 children it is £125
For 60 children it is £150
For 70 children it is £175
For 80 children it is £200
For 88 children it is £220

Figure 3.5b Janice's method

Janice (aged eight) worked out the cost of the school trip to a farm for the 88 children who went. Their methods of calculation (Figures 3.5a, b) were very different.

A teacher of second-year juniors (aged eight to nine) wrote about some work which arose from her class's outing:

> Following a visit to a waterbird sanctuary, the children wrote to the Coal Board to find out details of the rock structure below the nature reserve. They also found out about the age of the rocks. From this the more able children were asked to make a time-line, using strips of squared paper. The children worked out their own scale, and there were many strips of paper laid out on the classroom floor. Pam and Patti had so many strips that they realised that these could not be displayed on the classroom wall. James and Jason had the same problem, and worked out that they would need about 1000 sheets to complete the line.

We came together as a group and talked about the scales they had used, and how we should have to change them to fit on a shorter piece of paper. Pam and Patti had used a scale of 1 cm to 10 000 years, and that caused problems because we were going back so far in time. The children were asked to start a new time-line which would enable them to put their completed strip on one wall of the classroom. They measured the wall and worked out their scale accordingly. It became clear to me that they were extremely confident in handling and writing very large numbers, including millions.

Another teacher told of a different aspect of her children's understanding of very large numbers:

> The children were talking about the biggest number they could get. Shaun had 10 000 000. The biggest numbers they could produce all began with 1. Thinking about the calculator keys, I discussed with the children 'bigger than' up to nine. The children then realised that all nines would give them a bigger number. Shaun however said: 'I think the biggest number is billions and trillions, isn't it Sally?' Sally (aged six) replied that she didn't think there was an end to numbers.

An advisory teacher wrote about an incident that took place when he was working with a class of eight to nine-year-old children:

> The class were discussing large numbers, and in particular, one million. When asked to suggest ideas incorporating numbers up to one million, James suggested that there might be a million teeth in the school. He was asked what he would need to find out in order to test his idea. Someone else said that we would need to know how many teeth a child of their age would have. During this exploration, James came up with the number 50 000. I have to admit that at the time I didn't quite understand where he got it from, and there didn't seem to be time at that moment to listen to a full explanation! A discussion about first and second teeth continued for a little time, but was interrupted by the class teacher exclaiming that she had just done on paper the calculation that James had evidently done in his head. The 50 000 were people! He had used 20 as the average number of teeth for each person, and had worked out that it would need 50 000 people to have a million teeth altogether. We were truly amazed by his mental skill since James did not usually demonstrate high achievement. I admonished myself for not taking time to listen to his reasoning when he first made his contribution. The subsequent praise ensured that he forgave me – I think.

He explained how he had arrived at his answer. He thought that if everyone had only two teeth, 500 000 people would be needed. But since we have (about) 20 teeth, the answer would be one tenth of this, or 50 000.

In a class of nine-year-olds, Chris was doing an activity called 'The Ant Maze'. The object was to obtain the highest total by moving from one insect to the next, carrying out the mathematical operation written on each. Chris said:

'One times two equals two, times ten equals twenty, times ten equals two hundred, times two equals four hundred, times five equals two thousand, times five equals ten thousand, times two equals twenty thousand, times ten equals two hundred thousand, times two equals four hundred thousand, times five equals two million, times ten equals twenty million, times ten equals two hundred million, times ten equals ...'

He paused and reached for his calculator, but before he pressed any buttons he said: 'Ah, the calculator won't do it – there are too many numbers. Now where did I get to? Two hundred million ... two thousand million.'

If children are to become familiar with very large numbers, such as the millions and billions which now confront people in government information, the calculator gives a way in which children can gain this experience. Very little practical experience is possible for very large numbers – no school has a million Multilink cubes. A very few real visualisations of a million are possible for children. There are a million cubic centimetres in a cubic metre, but this is difficult to visualise because it is three-dimensional. However, Chris could probably calculate that because there are 100 centimetres in a metre, each layer of cubes in the cubic metre would contain 100×100 cubes, or 10 000 cubes; 100 layers of cubes would give $100 \times 10\,000$ cubes, or a million cubes. James might have been able to go on, after realising that 50 000 children would be needed for a million teeth, to work out that, in schools of 200 pupils, 250 schools would be needed to provide the million teeth.

Negative numbers

The project children were provided with simple four-function Texas Instruments TI–1103 calculators. These were very simple battery-operated machines with large clear keys. This model does not have a change-sign (+/–) key, so that it is not possible to key negative numbers directly into the calculator. However, the children were not long in finding negative numbers as the results of calculation. For example, the calculation:

$6 - 8 =$

gives the display:

Unfortunately, on this model of calculator the negative sign is not displayed immediately next to the number to which it relates; ideally the display should be:

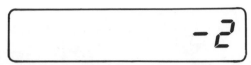

However, the children quickly spotted and asked about the negative sign, and number-lines had to be extended below zero:

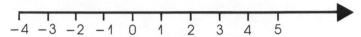

Soon, teachers were enquiring into children's knowledge of negative numbers. One teacher wrote:

The children were subtracting from 50 using dice and Dienes blocks. They were trying to get to 0. They wrote down 50 and subtracted the number shown on the die, using Dienes blocks as a check on their mental calculation. Jenny had 3 left and shook 5. She said: 'I can't take it away. I would owe two.' She tried this on a calculator and said: 'It is take away two.' She later tried to make other negative numbers, and she could do this. When given the problem:

The answer is –1. What is the question?

she produced a pattern of questions:

$1 - 2$
$2 - 3$
$3 - 4$
. . .
. . .

When asked what needed to be taken away from 100 to give –1, she said: 'Easy ... 101.' She said she always made the second number one bigger. She could use this method when the answer was –2, but not for –3.

Four out of five of Jenny's group could make negative numbers. Mark wrote down:

$0 - 1 = -1$ $-1 - 0 = -1$

Lucy said: 'I can use big numbers' and wrote:

$10\,000 - 1\,000\,001$ is –1

and before I could ask her to check it on the calculator, she had amended it to:

$10\,000 - 10\,001$ is –1.

One teacher invented a game in which negative numbers were likely to turn up naturally. The game was called 'Smarties', and the rules were as follows:

- Before starting this game, children count and sort a tube of Smarties, and make a block graph of the colours of the Smarties. Suppose there are 31 Smarties in the tube. Each child receives 31 points to start the game.

- The Smarties are returned to the tube at the beginning of the game. They are taken out one by one, and each child records a guess as to which colour will come out next.

I guess red yellow brown black yellow orange green black yellow Pink green orange brown red green green Pink orange black yellow purple red black brown purple red all of the pink have gone orange red green brown black red all of the reds have gone brown purple orange orange all of the browns have gone orange green all of the blacks have gone orange all of the yellows have gone purple all of the greens have gone orange all of the orange

I have 31 points

31 − 2 = 29	5 − 2 = 3
29 − 2 = 27	3 − 2 = 1
27 − 2 = 25	1 − 2 = −1
25 + 2 = 27	−1 + 2 = 1
27 − 2 = 25	1 − 2 = −1
25 − 2 = 23	−1 − 2 = −3
23 − 2 = 21	−3 − 2 = −5
21 + 2 = 23	−5 − 2 = −7
23 − 2 = 21	−7 − 2 = −9
21 − 2 = 19	−9 + 2 = −7
19 − 2 = 17	−7 + 2 = −5
17 − 2 = 15	−5 − 2 = −7
15 + 2 = 17	−7 + 2 = −5
17 − 2 = 15	−5 − 2 = −7
15 − 2 = 13	−7 − 2 = −9
13 − 2 = 11	−9 − 2 = −11
11 − 2 = 9	−11 − 2 = −13
9 − 0 = 7	−13 − 2 = −15
	−15 − 2 = −17
	−17 + 2 = −15
	−15 + 2 = −13

Figure 3.6

■ Correct guesses score 2 points.
Incorrect guesses lose 2 points.

The teacher wrote about what happened:

◖ **Number-lines and calculators are available for this game. Children are encouraged to consult the graph and to work out a probable colour to appear next. They often record when all the Smarties of one colour are out. A tube containing 31 Smarties is useful; it gives experience of moving up and down the number-line on odd numbers. Negative numbers appear naturally, so the number-line should stretch below zero. Much of the calculation of scores will be mental, but calculators and number-lines are available for checking.** ◗

A child's recording of this game is shown in Figure 3.6.

Another teacher devised a game called 'Take a Score'. Each child had a record sheet, as shown in Figure 3.7.

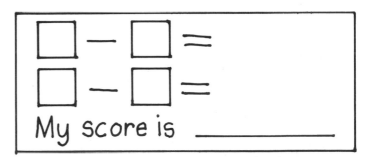

Figure 3.7

Each child threw a die four times; after each throw the score was written in one of the boxes. The calculations were then made, and the total score was the sum of the two answers. Negative answers might arise in the subtractions, and the addition of both positive and negative numbers might be needed to find the total score. In this classroom some calculators with change-sign (+/−) keys (such as the TI–1106, subsequently replaced by the TI–106) were available, and it was possible to input negative numbers when checking results on the calculator.

The teacher wrote:

> 🔲 **Jamie and Allen were playing a variation on the 'Take a Score' game. Jamie's book looked like this when I spoke to him:**
>
> 0 – 8 = 8
> 0 – 5 = 5
>
> **My score is 13.** 🔳

The conversation between Jamie and his teacher went as follows:

Teacher: Do you think those two are right?

Jamie: Yes.

Teacher: Will you check them with the Unifix, please?

Jamie: Is it –8?

Teacher: What can you use to check it?

[Jamie used a calculator, and corrected the subtractions.]

Teacher: What do you think your score is?

Jamie: [Using fingers and speaking to himself.] Minus four.

Teacher: How do you get that?

Jamie: Well, I said my thumb was –8, and then I counted –7, –6, –5, –4. Oh, I should have said –7, –6, –5, –4, –3. It's –3.

Teacher: Do you want to check it?

Jamie: [Enters –8 + –5 = on the calculator.] Oh, it's –13.

Teacher: Is the calculator right? Why does it say –13?

Jamie: 'Cos –8 and –5 is –13.

In another classroom, children were making up their own questions about negative numbers, such as $(-1)+(-3)=(-4)$ and $(-2)-(-3)=-1$. Some answers were right, some were wrong. If children are to be given experience of the behaviour of the addition and subtraction of negative numbers, a calculator is needed on which negative numbers can be keyed in directly by using the change-sign key. However, even without this aid, one child said that he knew that $(+1)-(-1)$ had to be 2 because there was a difference of 2 between +1 and –1. Another child said that of course –4 was less than 2, because it was further back on the number-line.

In one classroom, a problem arose when a child wanted to know what happened when two negative numbers, –3 and –3, were multiplied together. The teacher was unsure what the answer should be, and the basic four-function calculators available in that classroom could not cope with the calculation. When a calculator which handled negative numbers satisfactorily was found, teacher and child learnt together.

Children began to make use of negative numbers in their mental calculations. The method of subtraction shown in Figure 3.8 was discovered independently in several classrooms, by children who liked to work from the left-hand end of a calculation. The child whose work is shown writes the result of the calculation on the first line, and then records an explanation of the steps used.

Thus, children who use calculators quickly become able to interpret negative displays on the calculator, and to make sense of negative numbers in situations in which their use is appropriate. The teachers have been ingenious in devising situations, such as the 'Smarties' game, which were within the children's comprehension and where it was necessary to extend the number-line below zero. Children have also found their own uses for negative numbers, such as the subtraction method shown in Figure 3.8.

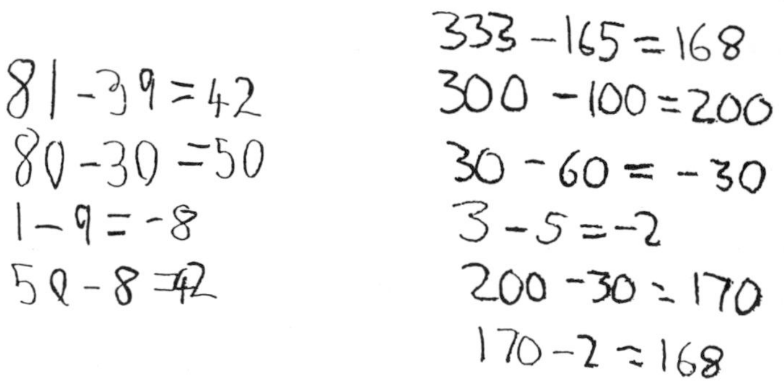

81 – 39 = 42
80 – 30 = 50
1 – 9 = –8
50 – 8 = 42

333 – 165 = 168
300 – 100 = 200
30 – 60 = –30
3 – 5 = –2
200 – 30 = 170
170 – 2 = 168

Figure 3.8

Decimals and fractions

As soon as they start to use the division key on the calculator, children see decimal numbers in the display. At the end of the first year of CAN, the evaluator, after a visit to a project classroom, wrote about an incident in which a six-year-old child had consulted her:

> 🔲 **A girl brought me a calculator displaying 3.125. 'Do you know about numbers like this?' she asked. When I said I did, she showed me what she had been doing. 'We are doing things about fifty,' she said, 'but I thought I would like to halve it.' She showed me 25, halved again and showed me 12.5, halved again to produce 6.25, and finally obtained 3.125.**
>
> **I suggested that halving was like sharing things between us, so we shared 25 cubes between us. She gave us 12 each, but said she couldn't halve the one left over. 'Let's make a Plasticine cube and then we can cut it in half,' I said. 'How many have we got?' 'Twelve and a half,' she replied. Then I invited her to try it on the calculator. 'Is that how the calculator writes a half?' she asked.**

We went on to make six and a quarter, using the Plasticine and consulting the calculator. She accepted that the calculator wrote six and a quarter as 6.25. She insisted on going on: 'So that's how the calculator writes three and an eighth.' She commented that the numbers were getting longer, but her confidence in matching the Plasticine with the calculator display seemed undaunted. ▄

Similar experiences occurred in many classrooms, and many children came to know that '0.5 is the way the calculator writes a half'. For example, a teacher asked Nigel, a low-attaining eight-year-old, to explore patterns of dividing by two, initially without a calculator. She started him off with the sequence $10 \div 2 = 5$, $12 \div 2 = 6$, $14 \div 2 = 7$. Nigel continued, using the calculator, and recorded:

$15 \div 2 = 7.5$, $\qquad 16 \div 2 = 8$, $\qquad 17 \div 2 = 8.5$.

The teacher asked him to predict the answer to $23 \div 2$, which he did correctly and confidently.

For many children, a stream of figures after the decimal point is at first a great surprise. An advisory teacher interviewed Gail, another low-attaining eight-year-old, and part of their conversation went as follows:

Teacher: Can you share 16 sweets between three people?

Gail: They will all get five and there will be one left over.

Teacher: Do you ever use the calculator for sharing? Show me.

[Gail put in $16 \div 3$ and got 5.3333333.]

Teacher: What does it mean?

Gail: I think it's wrong.

Later, Gail explained to the advisory teacher, in response to $13 \div 2 = 6.5$: 'That's how much they get. The point five is the bit left over.'

Some teachers have devised activities which ensure that children meet decimals. One activity was a workcard which started a pattern (Figure 3.9). Children investigated the pattern in different ways. David used Unifix.

David: Two lots of three – that's six. That's too many ... I want five. Two lots of two is four. It must be two and a half.

Teacher: Can you check that on the calculator?

[David keyed in $2 \times 2.5 =$]

Some children extended the pattern to much larger numbers, and some explored three times and four times. Figure 3.10 shows part of a child's work on this activity.

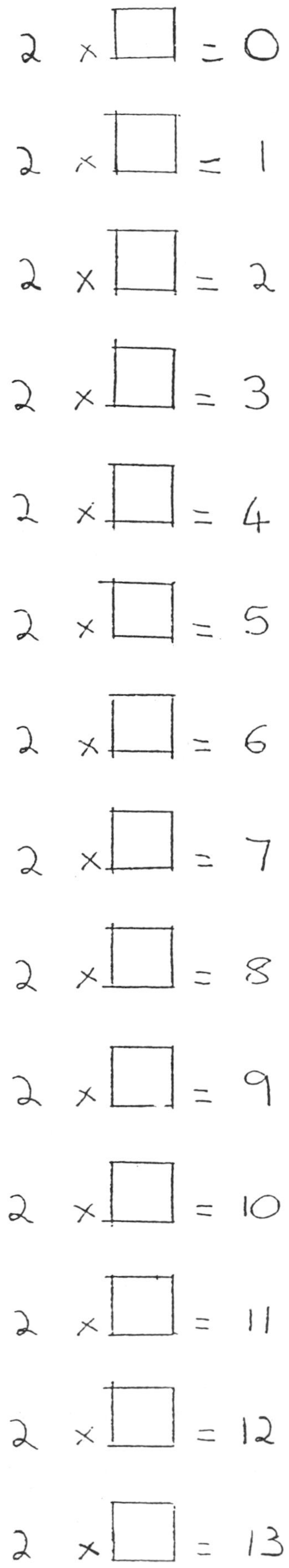

$$2 \times \square = 0$$
$$2 \times \square = 1$$
$$2 \times \square = 2$$
$$2 \times \square = 3$$
$$2 \times \square = 4$$
$$2 \times \square = 5$$
$$2 \times \square = 6$$
$$2 \times \square = 7$$
$$2 \times \square = 8$$
$$2 \times \square = 9$$
$$2 \times \square = 10$$
$$2 \times \square = 11$$
$$2 \times \square = 12$$
$$2 \times \square = 13$$

Figure 3.9

$2 \times 48 = 96$

$2 \times 48.5 = 97$

$2 \times 49 = 98$

$2 \times 49.5 = 99$

$2 \times 50 = 100$

I found a pattern.

When you take a number, for instance, 40. 2×40 equals 80. You know you can't make 81 by multiplying numbers like 1, 2, 3, 4 etc. etc so you have to use a half. So you take 40 and 40 to make 80 then you take two 0.5 (A HALF) you get 1 so you would be getting 80 and 1 = 81. That happens with all of the numbers.

$4 \times 0 = 0$

$4 \times 0.25 = 1$

$4 \times 0.5 = 2$

$4 \times 0.75 = 3$

$4 \times 1 = 4$

$4 \times 1.25 = 5$

$4 \times 1.5 = 6$

$4 \times 1.75 = 7$

I found out that in the calculator a quarter is 0.25, two quarters 0.5 and three quarters 0.75. So four 0.25s is 1

Figure 3.10

A teacher asked a group of first-year junior children (aged seven to eight): 'How could we show fractions on a calculator?' None of them knew, so she took an example, and wrote down the fraction $^1/_4$. She said: 'The way we write it – it contains the numbers one and four. What can you do with one and four on the calculator?' Gus recorded what he could do in a very systematic way; he wrote:

$$4 + 1 = 5 \qquad 1 + 4 = 5$$
$$4 \times 1 = 4 \qquad 1 \times 4 = 4$$
$$4 - 1 = 3 \qquad 1 - 4 = -3$$
$$4 \div 1 = 4 \qquad 1 \div 4 = 0.25$$

Then he said: 'I think a quarter is 0.25.' And he checked it in two ways:

$$0.25 + 0.25 + 0.25 + 0.25 = 1$$
$$0.25 \times 4 = 1$$

The child's work shown in Figure 3.11 is the familiar activity of putting a number in the middle of a square, and then putting a number at each of the four corners, these four numbers adding up to the number in the middle. The child's sketch may not be very accurate, but it shows clear appreciation that 1.5 is half way between 1 and 2, and that 1.75 is half way between 1.5 and 2.

One teacher gives an extended account of work on decimals done by a group of eight to nine year olds:

■ One group became very interested in the remainders in division, and on their calculator checks. They had:

$43 \div 2 = 21$ rem 1   Check: 21.5
$41 \div 3 = 13$ rem 2   Check: 13.666666

I asked them about $40 \div 3$. That was easy: 13 rem 1. On the calculator? 'Thirteen point something.' They did the following calculations mentally and checked them on the calculator:

$40 \div 3 = 13$ rem 1   Check: 13.333333
$39 \div 3 = 13$ Check: 13.
$38 \div 3 = 12$ rem 2   Check: 12.666666

They were able to predict the next calculation:

$37 \div 3 = 12$ rem 1   Check: 12.333333

and they continued the pattern down to $27 \div 3 = 9.0$.

I returned and asked: 'Why .333333 and .666666?' They were not sure. We recalled:

$49 \div 2 = 24$ rem 1   Check: 24.5

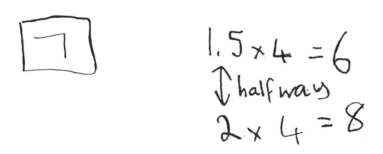

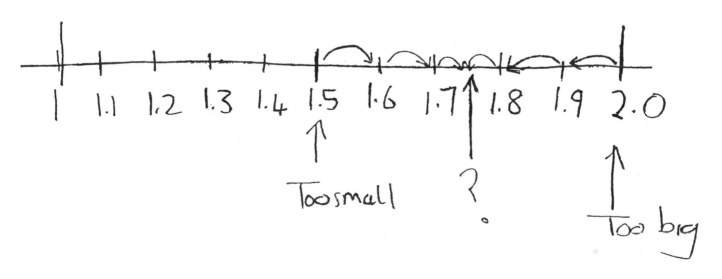

Figure 3.11

They said that point five is a half, and remainder one when dividing by two is a half. One of them then suggested that .333333 was three quarters. 'No,' the other said. 'Point seven five is three quarters and point two five is one quarter.'

So we got out the fraction cakes and shared between three people. They realised that 4 ÷ 3 = 1 rem 1, and that in dividing by three, remainder one is one third. We returned to the calculator, and recorded:

40 ÷ 3 = 13 rem 1 or 13.333333

The children said: '.333333 is one out of three, or a third.'

41 ÷ 3 = 13 rem 2 or 13.666666

The children said: '.666666 is two out of three, or two thirds.'

Many children have built up a good deal of knowledge of the decimal equivalents of familiar fractions, but the calculator does not make it plain **why** it writes fractions in these ways. This is a much more difficult task.

Ways of developing this idea include working with sums of money such as £0.50, £0.25 and £0.33. Children also need to explore ways in which the calculator writes fractions such as $^1/_{10}$ and $^1/_{100}$, and relate this to their understanding of place value for whole numbers.

The following conversation between a teacher and two nine-year-old children shows the children's developing awareness of why the calculator writes fractions as it does. They were again doing the familiar activity of putting a number in a box, and writing numbers at the corners (Figure 3.12).

The teacher asked Michael and Richard to explain:

Teacher: Can you tell us what you've done, Michael?

Michael: Nought point two five, and you add them all together and you get one.

Teacher: You seem to know that. ... How do you know that?

Michael: Put one ... divide by four.

Richard: 'Cos ... point two five is a quarter ... I was just playing around with the calculator ... when I was in the infants ... I just found it out.

Teacher: But how do you know it is a quarter? ... What if someone didn't believe you? How could you prove it to them?

Michael: Because 25 is a quarter of 100, and if you add a nought on the beginning, it would be a quarter of one as well.

Carole, working on the same activity, sometimes recorded in decimals and sometimes in fractions (Figure 3.13).

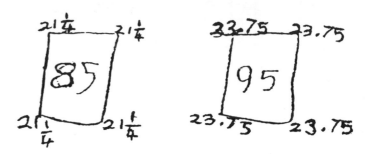

Figure 3.13

The decimal equivalent of one third shows a further complication. The calculator gives:

1 ÷ 3 = 0.3333333

but on most four-function calculators:

0.3333333 × 3 = 0.9999999

However, all children will have to tackle this rounding problem in the mathematics National Curriculum:

Know how to interpret results on a calculator which has rounding errors.

Example: *Interpret* 7 ÷ 3 × 3 = 6.9999999 *if it occurs on a calculator.* [AT 4, Level 4]

In fact, as children explore numbers with their calculators, they become more familiar with the structure of the number system than they could in any other way at this age. Their developing knowledge includes not only whole numbers, positive and negative, but also decimal numbers.

Most children in the project have not yet reached a full understanding of decimals, although they can use them in many situations, as can be seen from the examples above. The mistakes in James' work, shown in Figure 3.14, indicate what is lacking in his understanding of decimal place value. He makes a consistent error whenever he has to add or subtract a number with one decimal place from a number with two decimal places; he treats the decimal

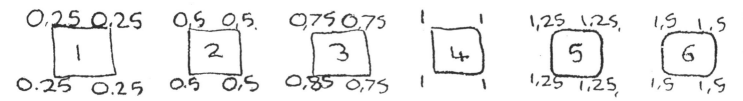

Figure 3.12

$$8.04 + 0.17 = 8.21 \quad 8.21 - 3 = \underline{5.21}$$

$$2.29 + 0.1 = 2.30 \quad 2.30 + 2 = \underline{4.30}$$

$$0.23 + 0.12 = 0.35 \quad 0.35 + 9 = \underline{9.35}$$

$$7.32 + 0.2 = 7.34 \quad 7.34 - 1 = \underline{6.34}$$

$$3.31 - 0.3 = 3.28 \quad 3.28 - 12 = \underline{5.28}$$

$$8.28 + 0.3 = 8.31 \quad 8.31 - 5 = \underline{3.31}$$

Figure 3.14

parts as if they were whole numbers. If he were urged to check with the calculator, this would cause a conflict between what he thought and what the calculator showed. This might lead him to further exploration and to developing his understanding.

In order to help children to make sense of the number system, teachers need to develop a new teaching skill. Children find out from their calculators **how** numbers behave, but the calculator does not show **why** numbers behave like this. The teacher must devise activities which enable children to make sense of what they have found out from the calculator.

In the past, teachers have been able to keep negative numbers and decimals hidden from children until they thought the children would understand a full explanation. This is no longer a possible teaching strategy; children cannot be prevented from discovering negative numbers and decimals for themselves on the calculator display at an early stage. Dealing with this situation makes new demands on the teacher. Negative numbers seem to have caused few problems, but decimals are conceptually much more difficult.

4 CALCULATION WITHOUT A CALCULATOR

Personal methods of calculation

As the children who were working on CAN became familiar with numbers, and with the operations of addition, subtraction, multiplication and division, they developed methods of doing some of these operations mentally. They found the calculator unnecessary and slow when the numbers were within the range with which they could personally cope. Many children have developed pride in not being dependent on the calculator, and prefer to use their own personal mental methods whenever possible. Many children have also extended this interest, and have devised their own non-calculator methods for calculations with numbers which are too large for mental calculation, and so which require the recording of intermediate results.

The children were not taught the traditional pencil-and-paper vertical methods of calculation, and it is interesting that although some children's own non-calculator methods for addition and multiplication are rather like the traditional pencil-and-paper methods, no child has devised a method of subtraction which resembles the traditional 'decomposition' subtraction method.

This chapter gives examples of children's mental calculation methods, as they have explained them to adults, and of their non-calculator methods for dealing with larger numbers. A few examples are also given of activities which require approximation, estimation, rounding and approximate calculation

Children's recording of their calculations

In all the published primary mathematics schemes which were in existence when CAN began, the teaching of the traditional pencil-and-paper vertical methods of calculation formed a very substantial part of the work. Schools were therefore asked not to use the 'number' part of the scheme, but to devise their own activities. Consequently, the children did not become familiar with the traditional vertical arrangement of calculations, and in all the classrooms the children seemed to take it for granted that mathematics is written in the same way that English is written – from left to right, and from top to bottom of the page. The signs on the calculator keys also suggested ways of recording, and it became natural for children to write down the keys they had pressed. They transferred this style of recording to their non-calculator calculations, and it became the usual method of recording in CAN.

In Figure 4.1, a child was exploring the number 900. Most of the recording is both accurate and mathematically correct, but two problems arise. First, the simple four-function calculator used cannot deal with numbers of more than eight digits, and it shows an error message when the answer is too large to fit the calculator display. The child recorded the answer to $810\,000 \times 810\,000$ exactly as he saw it on the calculator: E65610000; he gives no evidence that he realised that the answer had overflowed the display. Most children soon realise what has happened, and some think that the error message E stands for 'enormous'.

The second error arises from recording the key strokes exactly as they were pressed. For example, the child recorded:

$$450 \div 2 = 225 \div 2 = 112.5$$

This is a literal record of the key strokes that were pressed, but it breaks the mathematical convention that the expressions on each side of an equals sign should be numerically equal. The correct conventional recording would be:

$$450 \div 2 = 225 \qquad 225 \div 2 = 112.5$$

It is not surprising that children whose only experience of the equals sign is on the calculator should fall into this error. On the calculator, = does not indicate equality, but is the key that carries out the operation. Its role is the same as that of the RETURN key on a computer, which carries out an action. Some non-calculator experience of = is needed if children are to use the equals sign correctly in the conventional mathematical way.

The child whose recording is shown in Figure 4.2 had some experience of using the equals sign in another situation as well as on the calculator. In this class, the children had done a good deal of work with the 'equaliser' (a balance which is similar to a see-saw in operation); they had balanced different weights at different distances from the centre of the equaliser. They had used the = sign to record the fact that the two sides of the equaliser were balanced. Hence, it was natural for them to use the = sign in a statement about numbers, as a way of indicating that the numbers on both sides of the statement were equal. For example, six-year-old Mat correctly wrote:

$$56 \times 56 = 3100 + 36$$

although his writing is difficult to read, as he was not yet sure which way round to write 3.

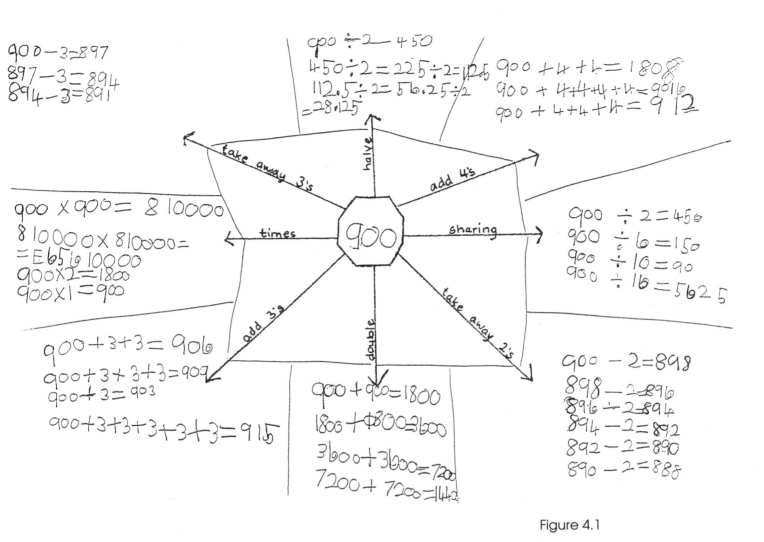

Figure 4.1

$$588 - 500 = 78 + 10 \quad \checkmark$$
$$54 + 65 - 85 = 12 + 41 = \text{NO}$$
$$53 \times 55 = 2300 + 685 \quad \text{Nearly}$$
$$56 \times 56 = £100 + £6 \quad \checkmark$$
$$255 - 245 = 300 - 290 \quad \checkmark$$
$$625 - 55 = 500 + 70 \quad \checkmark$$
$$566 = 500 + 66 \quad \checkmark$$

Figure 4.2

Addition

At the end of the first year of CAN, the headteacher of one school individually asked 12 top infant children, then aged seven, to work out $29 + 28$ in their heads, and explain to her how they had done it. Of these 12 children, two were unable to work out this sum in their heads, and needed apparatus to obtain a result. The remaining ten children all had slightly different methods, but all were able to make the calculation mentally. Some examples of these children's methods are:

◼ **Thirty and 30 are 60. Then you take away. Take away 1 for the 29, and take away 2 for the 28. So take away 3 altogether, and you get 57.**

Eight and 9 are 17 … 20 and 20 are 40 … 40 and 17 are 57.

The two 20s are four 10s, so that's 40. Add 9, which gives 49. Add 1, which makes 50. Then add the other 7, so that's 57.

Two 25s are 50. Then you have to add on 3 and 4, so you have to add on 7. It's 57. ◼

Of these four children, three started (in various ways) with the tens, and not with the units. It has become increasingly clear that this method of mental addition from the left is very common, but not universal.

In another school, some first-year junior children (aged eight) in their second year of CAN, were individually interviewed by an advisory teacher. The following conversation is typical:

Teacher: Can you add 42 and 27?

Child: Ninety-nine … no … 69.

Teacher: How did you do it?

Child: I added 20 and 40 and then the 7 and 2.

Teacher: Add 116 and 28.

Child: A hundred and forty-four.

Teacher: How did you do that?

Child: I added the tens together and then the units.

By the age of nine, most children were able to add two-digit numbers mentally, and many could add three-digit numbers. They often surprised visitors to the classroom by their excellent memory for the parts of a calculation, and by how little recording they needed to do.

Subtraction

A teacher described some children's mental subtraction methods when they began to calculate in their heads:

◼ **After becoming quite confident with subtraction number bonds up to 20, the children were encour-** aged **to find their own methods for subtraction problems.**

Several children took part of the number away to leave whole tens. For instance, when subtracting 7 from 56, Andrea took 6 from 56, giving 50, and then did $50 - 1 = 49$.

Jayne decided to add on for $31 - 7$, saying:

$7 + 8 = 15, 15 + 15 = 30, 30 + 1 = 31, 8 + 15 + 1 = 24.$ ◼

In Figure 4.3, two eight-year-olds write about their own subtraction methods. Both children started with the hundreds rather than with the units; many children prefer to do this.

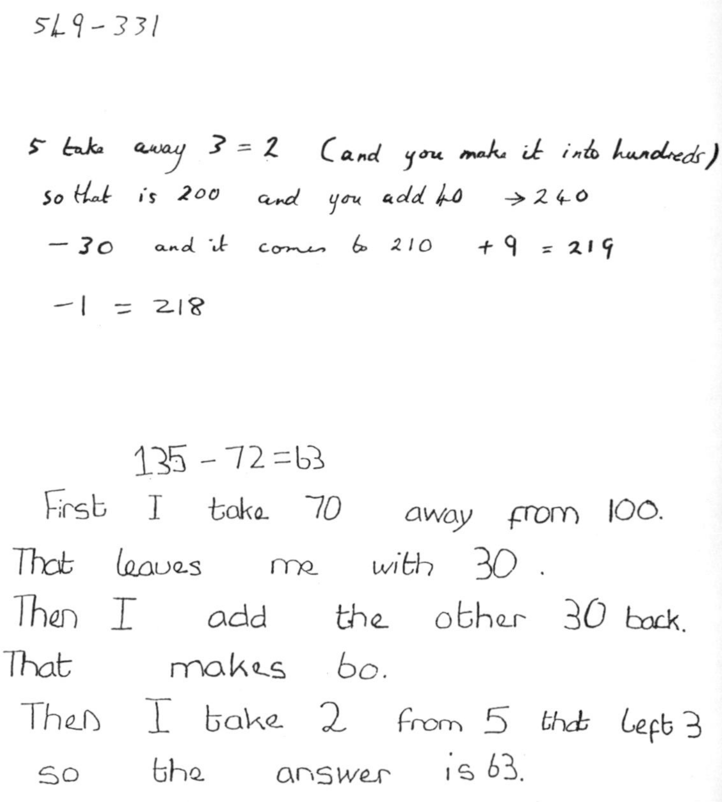

$549 - 331$

5 take away 3 = 2 (and you make it into hundreds)
so that is 200 and you add 40 → 240
-30 and it comes to 210 $+9 = 219$
$-1 = 218$

$135 - 72 = 63$
First I take 70 away from 100.
That leaves me with 30.
Then I add the other 30 back.
That makes 60.
Then I take 2 from 5 that left 3
so the answer is 63.

Figure 4.3

Some children make use of negative numbers. In one class (Figure 4.4), the teacher encouraged the children to record the answer at the top, with an explanation underneath. Mark (Figure 4.5) found mathematics very difficult. The teacher wrote:

◼ **Mark took a very long time to find a method of his own, but eventually (after many hiccups!) devised this method. Very uneconomical but – his own!** ◼

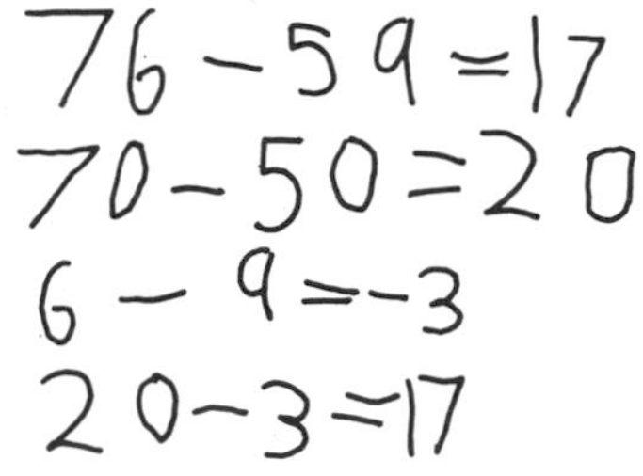

$$76 - 59 = 17$$
$$70 - 50 = 20$$
$$6 - 9 = -3$$
$$20 - 3 = 17$$

Figure 4.4

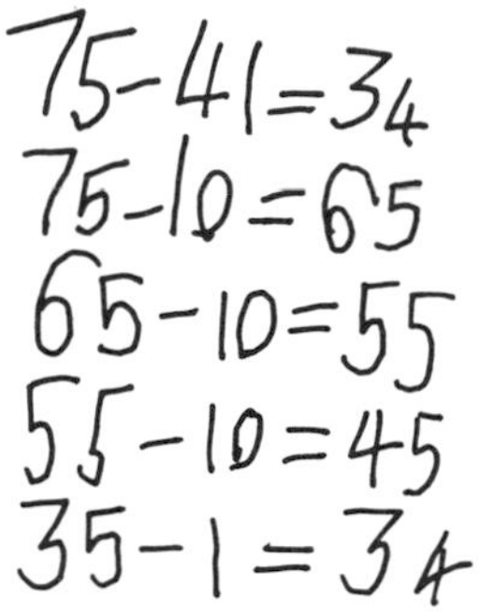

$$75 - 41 = 34$$
$$75 - 10 = 65$$
$$65 - 10 = 55$$
$$55 - 10 = 45$$
$$35 - 1 = 34$$

Figure 4.5

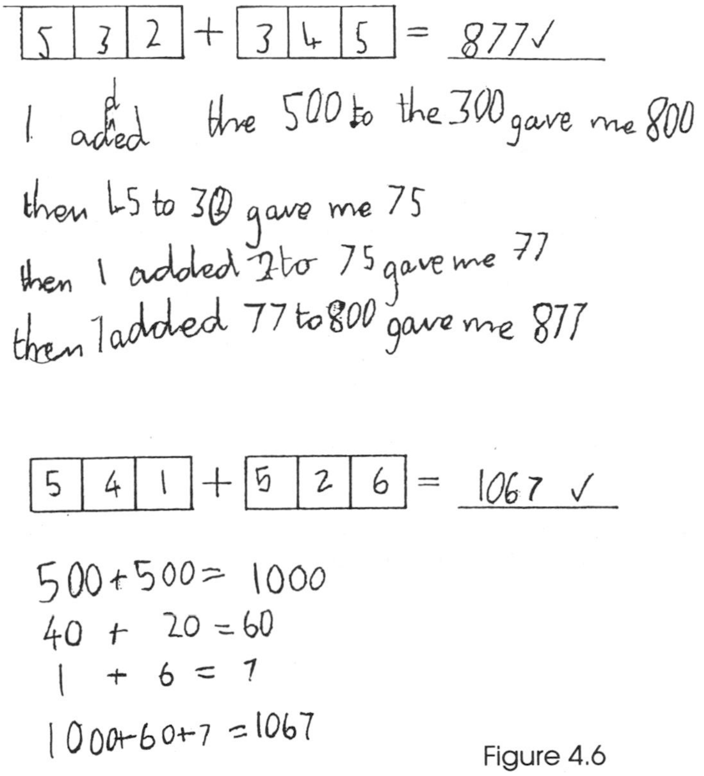

| 5 | 3 | 2 | + | 3 | 4 | 5 | = | 877 ✓ |

I aded the 500 to the 300 gave me 800

then 45 to 30 gave me 75

then I added 2 to 75 gave me 77

then I added 77 to 800 gave me 877

| 5 | 4 | 1 | + | 5 | 2 | 6 | = | 1067 ✓ |

$$500 + 500 = 1000$$
$$40 + 20 = 60$$
$$1 + 6 = 7$$
$$1000 + 60 + 7 = 1067$$

Figure 4.6

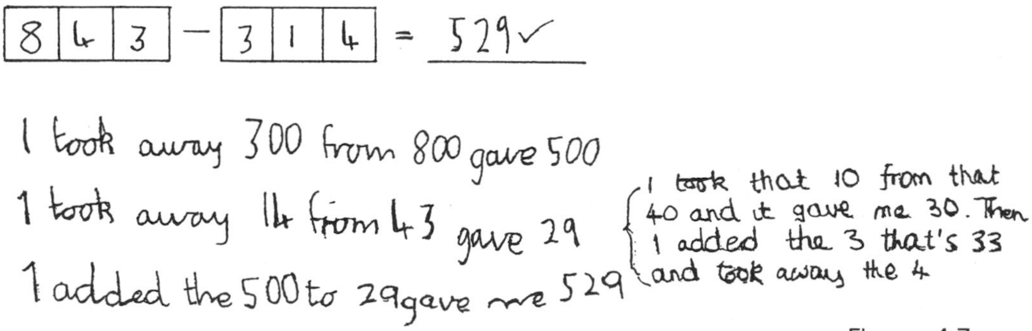

| 8 | 4 | 3 | – | 3 | 1 | 4 | = | 529 ✓ |

I took away 300 from 800 gave 500

I took away 14 from 43 gave 29

I added the 500 to 29 gave me 529

{ I took that 10 from that 40 and it gave me 30. Then I added the 3 that's 33 and took away the 4

Figure 4.7

In one school, in the third year of CAN, a teacher explored how her nine-year-olds would cope with the following from mathematics Attainment Target 3 at Level 4:

> . . . *without a calculator add or subtract two 3-digit numbers.*

Eleven-year-olds of average attainment are expected to succeed on this target. The teacher provided a worksheet on which children wrote how they had done their calculations mentally. Figures 4.6 and 4.7 show examples of, respectively, addition and subtraction.

For the subtraction of numbers of up to three digits, mental calculation, or calculation without a calculator, does not seem to cause many problems to nine-year-olds in the project. When larger subtractions are necessary, children use a calculator.

Multiplication

Without a calculator, the multiplication and division of large numbers are much more difficult than are addition and subtraction. Whatever methods children use, they usually need to record some intermediate results. However, some children have mental methods for multiplying by single-digit numbers, as two teachers explain. The children quoted here multiplied the tens before the units:

◼ **I asked Errol to try 36 multiplied by 3 mentally. He quickly said it was 108, and explained that three 30s made 90, three 6s made 18, and 90 and 18 was 108. I then asked him to do 13 multiplied by 36. Taking a little longer, he said 468. He explained that it was four lots of 108 add 36.**

I asked the children to explain how they worked

out 48×5. One said: 'Fifty times 5 is 250, and you take away 10, so it's 240.' Another child did 36×5 as 30 × 5 = 150 and then 6 × 5 = 30. ▉

A second-year junior child, Hannah, decided to develop her own method for multiplying two two-digit numbers without a calculator. She was proficient at adding and subtracting two-digit numbers mentally, so she tried the same method. She set herself to multiply 54 by 62, and after she had completed the task she wrote an account of what she had done (Figure 4.8). This account omits her learning process, but her teacher was able to describe in detail what happened. Hannah first multiplied 50 by 60 and obtained 3000; then she multiplied 4 by 2 and obtained 8. She added the two results together to give 3008. She thought the process was now finished, and she checked her result on the calculator. She was very surprised that the calculator gave the result as 3348. Hannah puzzled for some time about the difference of 340 between her result and that of the calculator, and

eventually she realised that the calculator had done two additional multiplications: 4×60 and 50×2. Her own account gives the multiplications in a different order, and also applies the method to 82×24, showing a neat method of recording what she had done. Her method is, in fact, the long multiplication algorithm, although it is not recorded in the conventional way.

Marion, too, was close to inventing the long multiplication algorithm (Figure 4.9). Examples of work on areas and volumes by some Welsh-speaking children are shown in Figure 4.10.

All these examples of children's work illustrate the fact that methods of non-calculator calculation with large numbers always depend on breaking down the large numbers into parts that can be handled mentally. The children in the examples have described in detail their individual methods of breaking down the calculation.

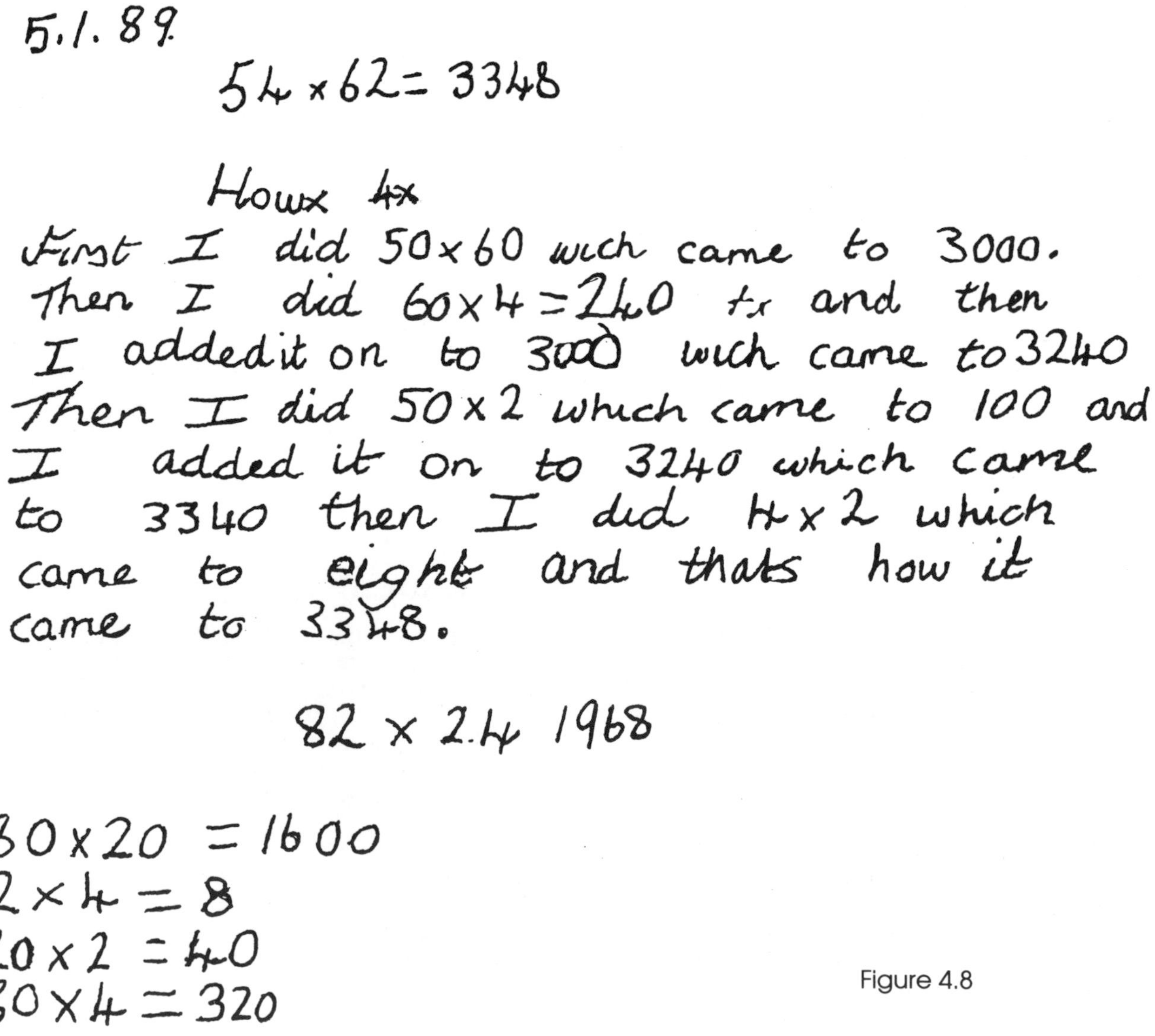

5.1.89.

$54 \times 62 = 3348$

How x 4x

First I did 50×60 wich came to 3000. Then I did $60 \times 4 = 240$ to and then I added it on to 3000 wich came to 3240 Then I did 50×2 which came to 100 and I added it on to 3240 which came to 3340 then I did 4×2 which came to eight and thats how it came to 3348.

82×24 1968

$80 \times 20 = 1600$
$2 \times 4 = 8$
$20 \times 2 = 40$
$80 \times 4 = 320$

Figure 4.8

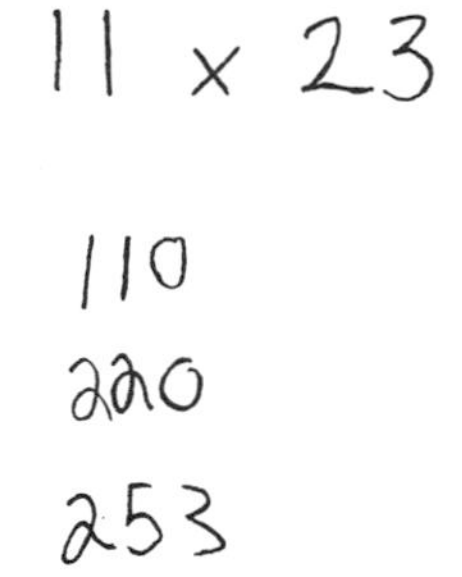

11×23

110

220

253

Figure 4.9

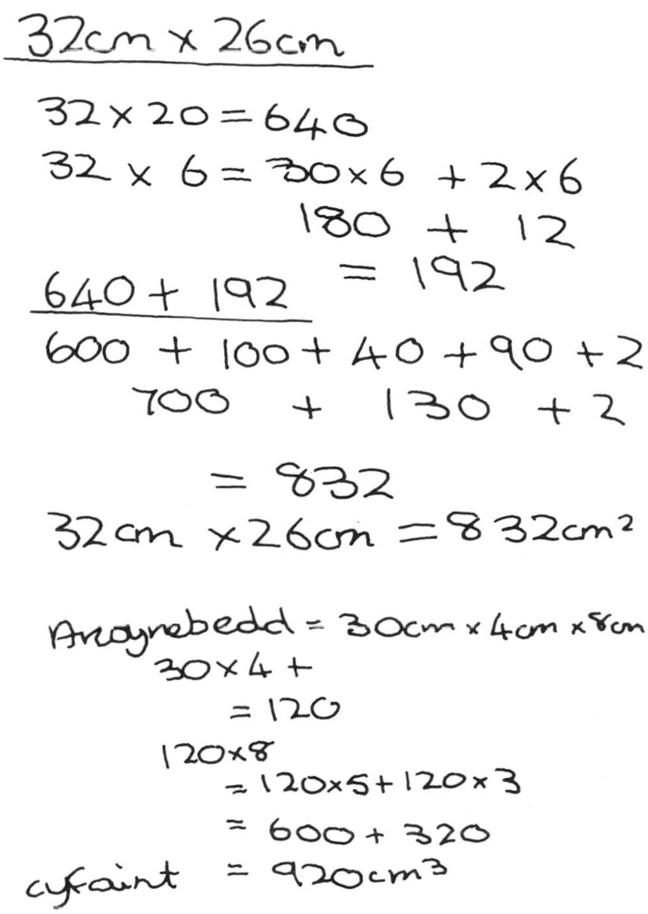

$32cm \times 26cm$

$32 \times 20 = 640$

$32 \times 6 = 30 \times 6 + 2 \times 6$

$\qquad\qquad 180 + 12$

$\qquad\qquad\quad = 192$

$640 + 192$

$600 + 100 + 40 + 90 + 2$

$\;700 \quad + \quad 130 \; + 2$

$\qquad\qquad = 832$

$32cm \times 26cm = 832cm^2$

$Arwynebedd = 30cm \times 4cm \times 8cm$

$\quad 30 \times 4 +$

$\qquad = 120$

$\;120 \times 8$

$\qquad = 120 \times 5 + 120 \times 3$

$\qquad = 600 + 320$

$cyfaint \;= 920 cm^3$

Figure 4.10

Petra's method, shown in Figure 4.11, for multiplying a three-digit number by a two-digit number without a calculator is much less sophisticated. To calculate 129×37, she wrote down 129 thirty-seven times, but then had an efficient way of doing the addition. First she added the hundreds ten at a time, recording when she reached 1000. Then she added the 20s five at a time, recording each time she reached 100. The 9s were added ten at a time, and finally she added all her subtotals.

In all these examples, it is important to realise that any example is only a snapshot of a child's way of working at a particular calculation, on a particular day. Petra, who multiplied 129 and 37 by adding together 129 a total of 37 times, may have moved on to a more economical method the next day. The visitor who saw Petra at work was only present on one day.

The teacher of another child, Rebecca, was able to give an account of how the child's non-calculator multiplication method developed over a period of time, and with support from the teacher. At first, Rebecca (then aged eight) used repeated addition. She broke the number to be multiplied into parts, so that she tackled 68×7 by doing:

$60 + 60 + 60 + 60 + 60 + 60 + 60$

and

$8 + 8 + 8 + 8 + 8 + 8 + 8$

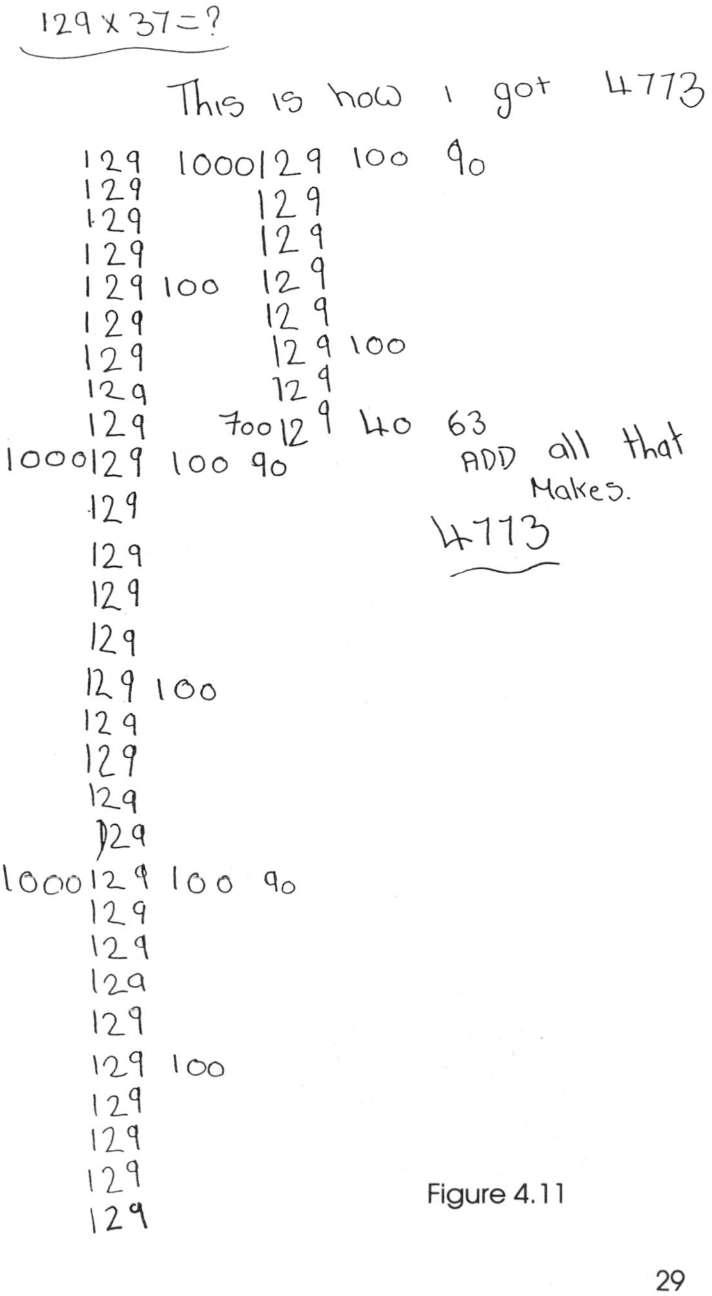

$129 \times 37 = ?$

This is how I got 4773

(repeated column of 129s with subtotals 1000, 100, 90, 129, 700, 40, 63)

ADD all that

Makes.

4773

Figure 4.11

She did not feel confident at adding 60s and 8s, so she broke these down further:

$$50 + 50 + 50 + 50 + 50 + 50 + 50 = 350$$
$$10 + 10 + 10 + 10 + 10 + 10 + 10 = 70$$ } = 420

$$5 + 5 + 5 + 5 + 5 + 5 + 5 = 35$$
$$3 + 3 + 3 + 3 + 3 + 3 + 3 = 21$$ } = 56

She finally obtained:

$$420 + 56 = 476.$$

The teacher thought that activities involving multiplication facts, such as 'Beat the Calculator' and 'Blockbusters', would lead Rebecca to a more efficient method. After these activities, Rebecca used multiplication for the units digit, but not for the tens or the hundreds! The teacher then devised an activity using dice and a layout sheet (Figure 4.12).

This had a dramatic effect on Rebecca's multiplication method; she now reduced her recording to a very efficient method:

$$243 \times 4 = 972$$

$$200 \times 4 = 800 \qquad 40 \times 4 = 160 \qquad 3 \times 4 = 12$$

She, too, had discovered a long multiplication method.

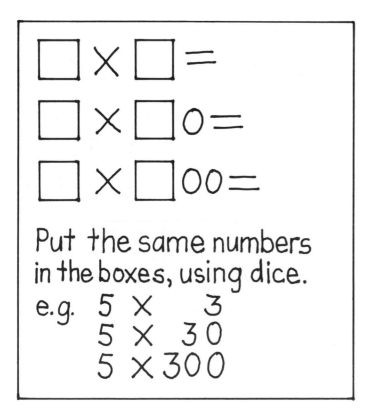

Figure 4.12

Division

Children find division by far the most difficult of the four arithmetical operations to carry out without a calculator. When children are 'making numbers' freely, the operation of division by two, or **halving,** appears much more frequently than does any other division (Figure 4.13).

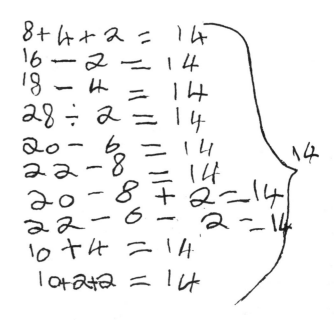

Figure 4.13

Earlier investigations into children's mathematics have indicated that many children are more comfortable with doubling and halving than they are with any other multiplications and divisions. The experience of CAN confirms this. Many children enjoy investigating halving, using their calculators and continuing into decimals (Figure 4.14).

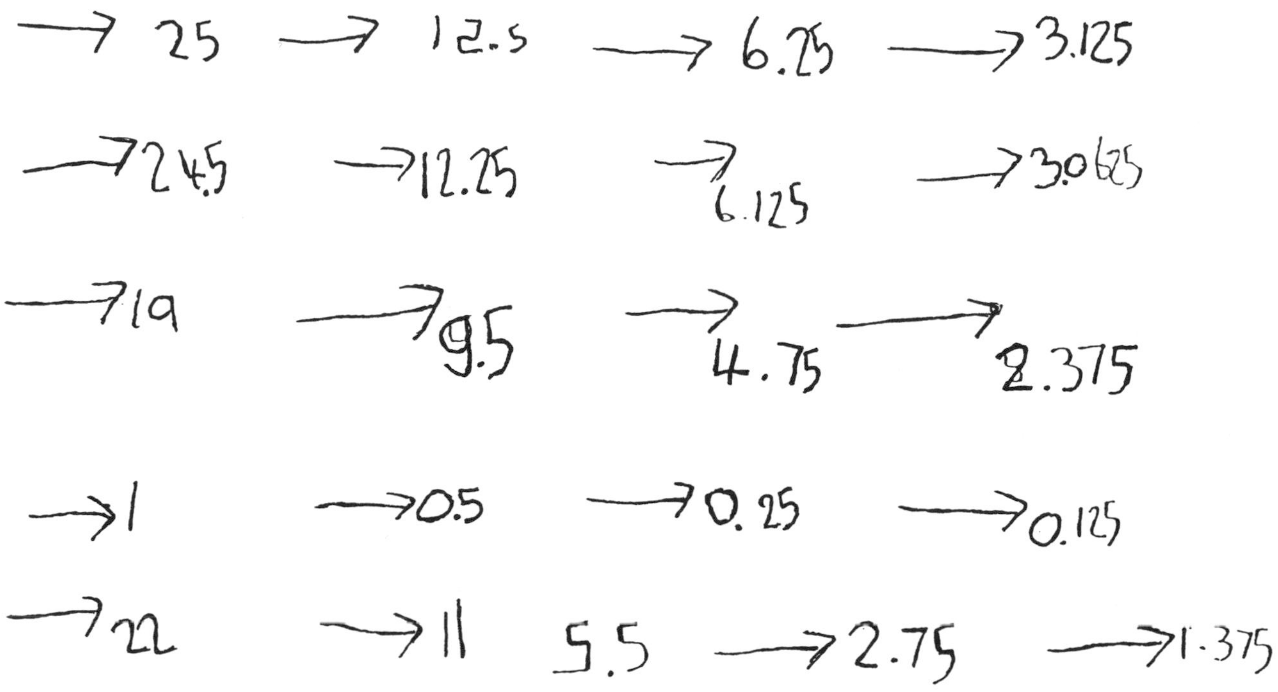

$\longrightarrow 25 \quad \longrightarrow 12.5 \quad \longrightarrow 6.25 \quad \longrightarrow 3.125$

$\longrightarrow 24.5 \quad \longrightarrow 12.25 \quad \longrightarrow 6.125 \quad \longrightarrow 3.0625$

$\longrightarrow 19 \quad \longrightarrow 9.5 \quad \longrightarrow 4.75 \quad \longrightarrow 2.375$

$\longrightarrow 1 \quad \longrightarrow 0.5 \quad \longrightarrow 0.25 \quad \longrightarrow 0.125$

$\longrightarrow 22 \quad \longrightarrow 11 \quad 5.5 \quad \longrightarrow 2.75 \quad \longrightarrow 1.375$

Figure 4.14

The familiar activity of making a number in a box from numbers at the corners can be extended to require division by asking for the same number to be put at each corner of the box. Bob and his teacher had the following conversation about the work shown in Figure 4.15:

Teacher: OK then, draw another pentagon. OK ... 34.

Bob: Six point eight ... I think.

Teacher: Do you want to check it?

Bob: Um ... 34 divided by 5 ... 6.8 ... yes, 6.8.

Teacher: So you could divide any number by 5? A really big one?

Bob: Yes ...107 ... 21.4.

Teacher: Have you checked it?

Bob: No, I think it's OK.

Teacher: What about this one?

Bob: Well ... 580 and 580 is 1160 ... oh ... no.

Teacher: You haven't actually written 1160. Is that the problem?

Bob: Oh, yes.

Teacher: How do you know where to put the decimal point?

Bob: Well ... I just know.

Teacher: Sort of common-sense?

Bob: Yes, I just know.

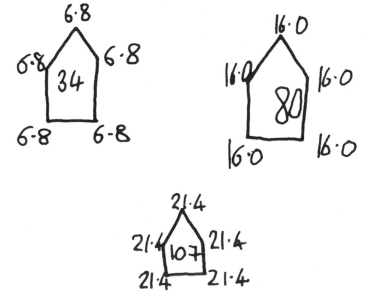

Figure 4.15

Rose Hip investigation

When we cut the rose hips open we found that there were diffrent amounts in each one there were 26, 27, 23, 24, 29, 26, 24, 19, 22, 26, 29, 25, we had to find out what the average amount of seeds. First of all we added all the numbers up then we had to divide that by twelve because that was the number of rose hips. And the answer was 25. This is how I worked it out I said half of 100 is 50 so there would be 6 50's in 300. Half of 50 is 25 so there would be 12 25's in 300. So 25 was the answer.

Figure 4.16

In Figure 4.16, Tessa explains how she divided to find an average. In the 12 rose hips which had been counted, there were 300 seeds altogether. She seems to have used her knowledge of multiplication, together with insight and some luck that the numbers were so convenient.

Clare describes her 'way of dividing' in Figure 4.17. She uses a mixture of multiplication and division, and copes nonchalantly with remainders.

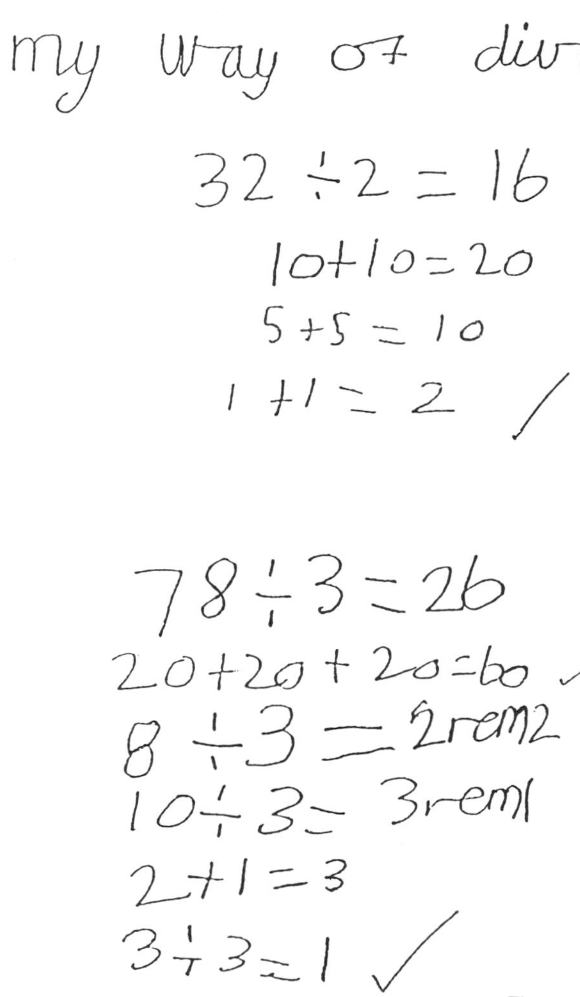

My Way of dividing

$$32 \div 2 = 16$$
$$10 + 10 = 20$$
$$5 + 5 = 10$$
$$1 + 1 = 2 \quad /$$

$$78 \div 3 = 26$$
$$20 + 20 + 20 = 60 \quad \checkmark$$
$$8 \div 3 = 2 \, rem \, 2$$
$$10 \div 3 = 3 \, rem \, 1$$
$$2 + 1 = 3$$
$$3 \div 3 = 1 \quad \checkmark$$

Figure 4.17

However, in view of the difficulty of the operation, it is not surprising that many children in the project had not, by the age of nine, yet found ways of dividing by a number of more than one digit without using their calculators.

Estimation, approximation and rounding

Estimation and approximation are very important skills in number work. These skills are as important for children who use calculators as they are for those who use pencil-and-paper methods. It is all too easy to press a wrong key on the calculator; everyone occasionally does

this. Sometimes these errors may not be very important, but if the first digit of a number is wrongly entered, this will have an important effect on the result of the calculation. It is therefore very important for children to know the size of answer to expect from a calculation. Making the estimate involves place value, approximation and mental calculation.

Estimation and approximation are usually mental activities which children do not record; the only trace that the child has estimated the answer is the correction of a wrong calculation. However, some teachers have provided activities which encourage children to record their estimates. Donna (Figure 4.18) was finding out how many bottles of milk the whole school drank in a day and in a week. The teacher encouraged her to round each number to the nearest ten and to make an estimate of the number of bottles for all the classes before she embarked on the detailed calculation (without a calculator). However, Donna did not make an estimate for the weekly total, and so she did not detect that her result was far from correct until the teacher asked her to do it again.

Carla was asked to estimate the results of subtractions to the nearest ten before making a detailed calculation. She was a child who subtracted from the left and used negative numbers. Her method of estimating is not clear, but it seems to be more sophisticated than simply rounding the original numbers to the nearest ten (Figure 4.19).

The examples of children's non-calculator calculations in this chapter show the variety of children's methods of calculation, and the ways in which these methods develop. Children inevitably base their methods of calculation, at a particular time, on their understanding of the number system at that time. Children who think of multiplication as repeated addition, and who do not yet know the multiplication facts, will use repeated addition as their multiplication method. Children who do not yet understand negative numbers cannot use them in subtraction. However, it seems that children make fewer errors in calculation when they use their own methods than do their contemporaries who learn traditional methods which are not their own.

One lesson from the CAN project is that, as children's understanding of the number system grows, they should be encouraged to refine their methods of non-calculator calculation, and to make these more efficient. It is important, however, that the improved method should continue to be the child's own method; mistakes creep in when children use methods that are not their own. An effective way of helping children to refine their methods is to encourage them to share their methods with others; children are often able to incorporate other children's ideas into their own methods of calculation.

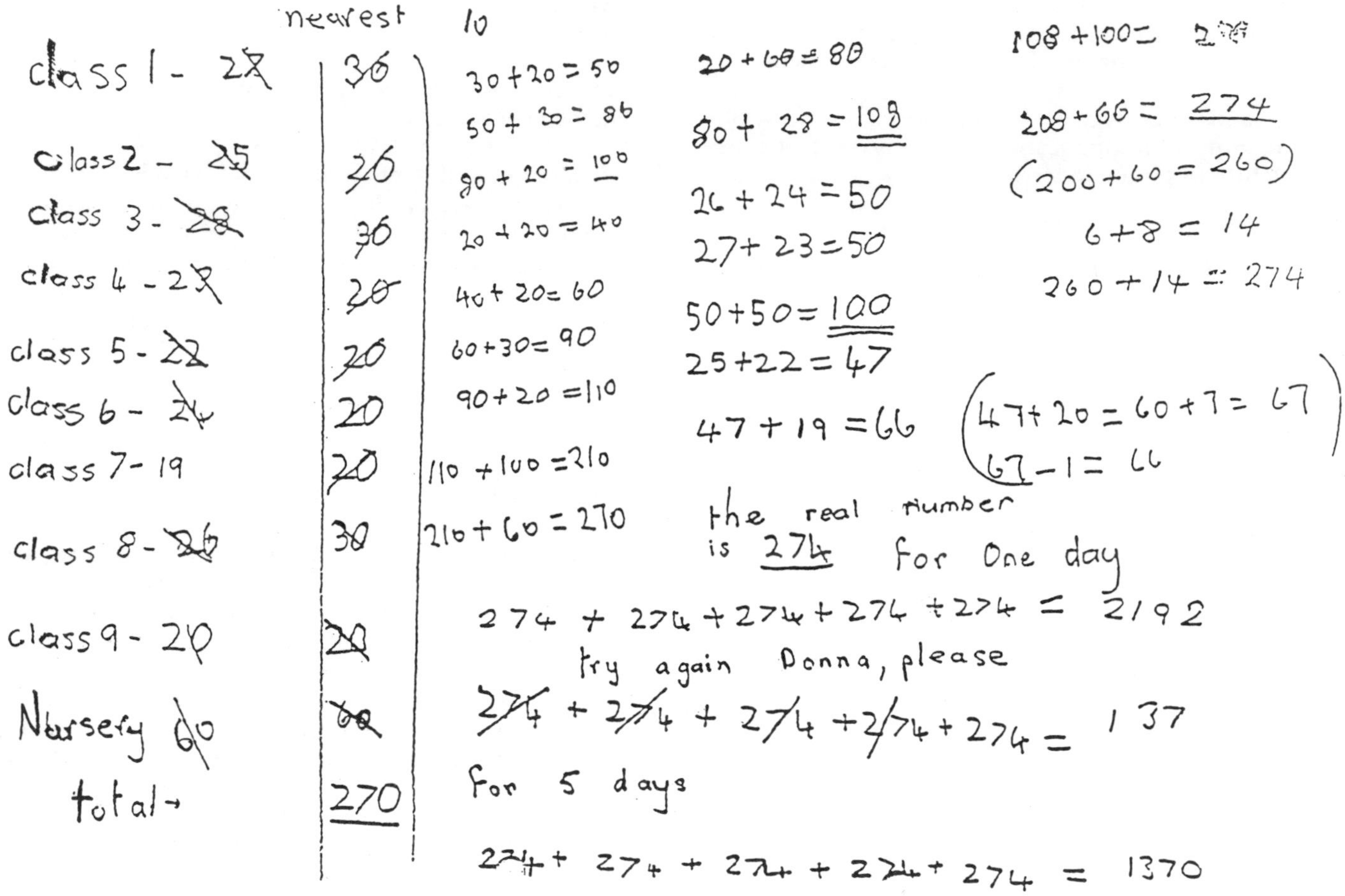

nearest 10

class 1 - 28   30

30 + 20 = 50   20 + 60 = 80   108 + 100 = 208

50 + 30 = 80   80 + 28 = 108   208 + 66 = 274

class 2 - 25   30

90 + 20 = 100   26 + 24 = 50   (200 + 60 = 260)

class 3 - 28   30

20 + 20 = 40   27 + 23 = 50   6 + 8 = 14

class 4 - 28   20

40 + 20 = 60   50 + 50 = 100   260 + 14 = 274

class 5 - 22   20

60 + 30 = 90   25 + 22 = 47

class 6 - 24   20

90 + 20 = 110   47 + 19 = 66 $\left(\begin{array}{l}47 + 20 = 60 + 7 = 67 \\ 67 - 1 = 66\end{array}\right)$

class 7 - 19   20

110 + 100 = 210

class 8 - 26   30

210 + 60 = 270

the real number
is 274   for One day

class 9 - 20   20

274 + 274 + 274 + 274 + 274 = 2192

Nursery 60   60

try again Donna, please

total →   270

274 + 274 + 274 + 274 + 274 = 137

for 5 days

274 + 274 + 274 + 274 + 274 = 1370

Figure 4.18

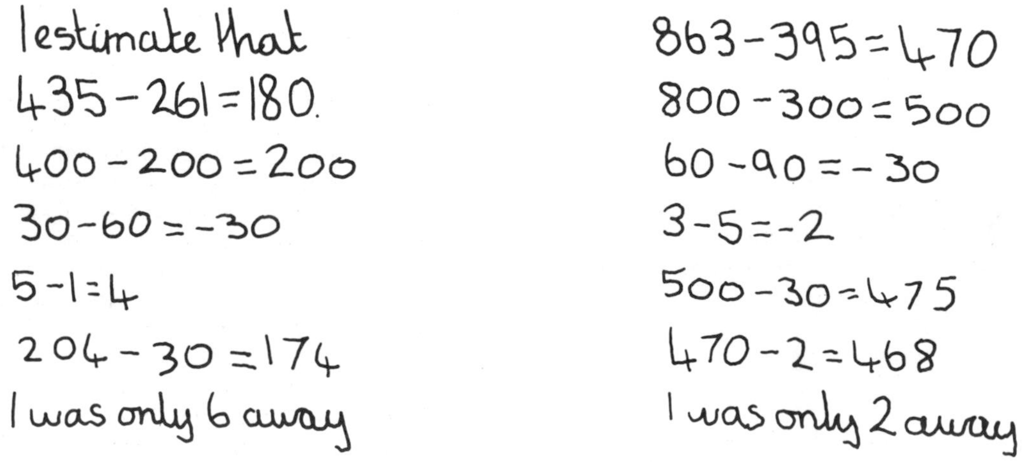

I estimate that
435 − 261 = 180.
400 − 200 = 200
30 − 60 = −30
5 − 1 = 4
204 − 30 = 174
I was only 6 away

863 − 395 = 470
800 − 300 = 500
60 − 90 = −30
3 − 5 = −2
500 − 30 = 475
470 − 2 = 468
I was only 2 away

Figure 4.19

USING AND APPLYING MATHEMATICS | 5

Introduction

The Cockcroft Report (DES 1982) emphasised the importance of applying mathematics to the solution of problems. It listed six important styles of teaching, which were recommended for mathematics teaching at all levels. These included:

Problem solving, including the application of mathematics to everyday situations.

Investigational work. [Para 243]

The Report explained the importance of problem solving:

The ability to solve problems is at the heart of mathematics. Mathematics is only 'useful' to the extent to which it can be applied to a particular situation and it is the ability to apply mathematics to a variety of situations to which we give the name 'problem solving'. [Para 249]

This theme has been built into the National Curriculum in mathematics, where Attainment Targets 1 and 9 are concerned with ***using and applying mathematics***. *Mathematics: Non-Statutory Guidance* (NCC 1989) identifies three objectives for using and applying mathematics:

- Acquiring knowledge, skills and understanding through practical work, through tackling problems and through using physical materials.

- Applying mathematics to the solution of a range of 'real life' problems, and to problems drawn from the whole curriculum.

- Exploring and investigating within mathematics itself.

From the beginning of CAN in 1986, teachers have encouraged children to ***use*** their mathematics to solve problems, and have asked them to investigate situations both within mathematics and in everyday life. Because children have not been required to learn standard methods for mathematical tasks, an investigational approach to mathematics has developed; many children have become much more able than their predecessors to explore mathematics, and to follow up their own ideas in their own way.

This chapter describes some of the ways in which teachers have helped children to use and apply their mathematics. The examples are classified under headings based on *Mathematics: Non-Statutory Guidance:*

- Practical tasks.
- 'Real life' problems.

- Problems within mathematics itself.

It is clear, however, that much classroom work based on using and applying mathematics does not fit neatly into a particular one of these categories, but spans several of them.

Practical tasks

Many practical classroom tasks, which either enable children to explore mathematical topics which are new to them or allow them to use the mathematics they already know, start from other activities. Neither teacher nor children necessarily expect that practical tasks will emerge. Two examples are given.

A class of six and seven-year-olds took part in a project which started from the story of the 'Big Friendly Giant' (Roald Dahl, *The B.F.G.*, Cape/Penguin). Among many other activities, they compared the size of their drawing of the giant with themselves. First they compared heights. The teacher wrote:

This proved to be quite a problem, and some did not really understand the process. Calculators were used to do the number work, which also involved using the decimal point.

The children also wrote about their work. This is an extract from one account:

I painted the face. He has blue eyes and rosy cheeks. He has odd shoes. They are red and blue and he has stripy socks. ... He is 2 metres and 89 centimetres tall. I am 1 metre and 21 centimetres tall. Then we thought about how much taller he was than me. He is 1 metre and 68 centimetres taller. It was a subtract sum.

The class then decided to compare the area of the drawing of the giant with similar drawings of the children. The teacher went on:

We chose four 'middle sized' children and drew round them and cut them out. The next problem came when we started pinning the cut-out shapes of the children over the giant. The children's arms and legs were sticking out and so not covering the giant properly. After much discussion one child finally came up with the idea of cutting off the arms of the children and sticking them on the giant's arms! From there we were able to go on to the idea

of cutting up the shapes of the children completely and sticking them on to the giant. It amazed the children that it needed six and a quarter 'middle sized' children to cover the giant.

She concluded:

The children learnt a lot – not to overlap when covering the giant, and to key the correct numbers into the calculator. It has also shown where I can help the children to develop: they were not good on conservation of area. When the shape of a child had been cut up, they all thought there was more.

This practical activity enabled the teacher to introduce the children to the new concept of area, in a situation where the children could all participate in the activity and join in the discussion.

In another school, a class of eight and nine-year-olds was doing a topic on 'Communications'. Several groups used bottles and water to investigate the pitch of sounds. Having used bottles of different sizes, some children decided to measure the capacity of the bottles. They made careful measurements, using litre measuring cylinders, and they found out how many millilitres there were in a litre. When Mike was starting to record his and Andrew's measurements, the teacher asked him how many millilitres there were in 1 litre 20 millilitres. He immediately replied 1020 millilitres, and volunteered that this was 102 centilitres. He also recorded it as 1.02 litres. Mike's recording is shown in Figure 5.1. The activity enabled him to show, in a practical way, his understanding of the conversion between different units of capacity.

Bottles	Label measurement	Our measurement
Wine bottle	litre 100cl	1 litre 20mls 1020 mls 102cls 1.02ls
Wine bottle	75cl	75cls 750mls 75cl 0.75
Wine bottle	100ml	720 mls 720 mls 72cls 0.72ls
Wine bottle	70cl	70cls 700mls 70cls 0.70ls
Wine bottle	no Label	70cls 700mls 70cl 0.70ls
Wine bottle 700ml		720mls 720ml 72cls 0.72ls
Lager bottle 300 mls		320mls 320 mls 32cls 0.32ls

Figure 5.1

My first attempt

I cut it out and immediately I knew it was wrong, because I did a square and five triangles on one corner. It should only have had 4 triangles: one on each side. I found out that corners are no good for joining. It is better for joining on the sides, but I did not put any flaps on either.

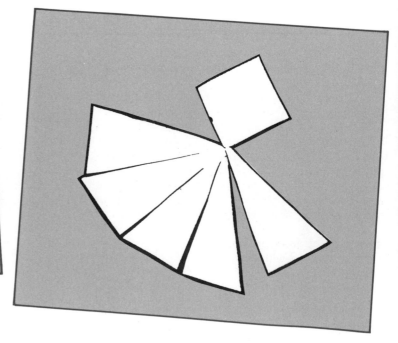

Figure 5.2a

Most of the examples in this book are concerned with number, for that was the original topic of CAN. However, children in the CAN project also do work on other aspects of mathematics, and the next example is a practical problem-solving activity on shape, devised by a teacher for a class of eight to nine-year-olds. The teacher gave them a practical problem on the packaging of products for sale. A week before, she had introduced the topic by setting up a display of attractive commercial cardboard boxes and packages, both intact and carefully unstuck to make visible the net from which the box was made. She then asked the children to choose a product and to design a package to contain it. In her account of her work, Sheila wrote:

We were asked to choose a solid shape. I chose one that looked like a tall Terry's Pyramint. The problem was I had to make it from one flat piece of paper.

Figures 5.2a, b, c show the development of Sheila's ideas. First she found out how to make a correct net, and then she found where to put flaps to stick the box together.

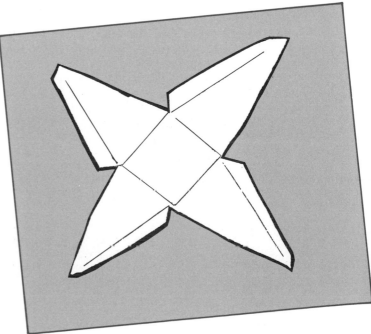

finally

Finally I did it agin and it was a lot better. I did it and I put some flaps on. I did some sharp edges. I glued it together and I stood it on the cupboard to dry.

My Second Attempt

My second attempt was a bit better but the problem was that it looked like arms and legs. The problem was that I had two extra triangles that were doing nothing.

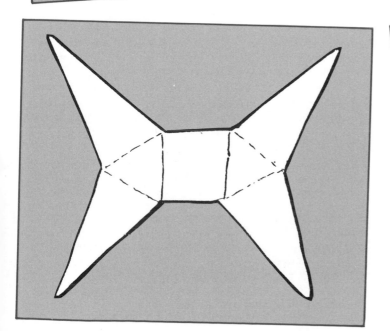

Figure 5.2b

Figure 5.2c

Real-life problems

It is probably misleading to enclose 'real life' in quotation marks, as if 'real-life' problems were only real life at second hand, or fiction masquerading as real life. Many real mathematical problems do arise in life, and problems drawn from real life can often be used in the classroom. Children may ask questions about reality which require mathematics to answer them. Children may also use mathematics to explore situations in the real life of the school or the neighbourhood. School visits provide starting points for a variety of follow-up work, including the mathematics of the real-life situation which was visited. Real events shown on television can sometimes provide a stimulus for mathematical exploration. Teachers in the CAN project have used all these types of starting point, and they have often responded to children's real-life questions and interests by encouraging them to use mathematics.

In the investigation of real life, situations are not always based on small whole numbers – real life is inconveniently full of large numbers and decimal numbers. However, the calculator enables children to calculate with large numbers and decimals as easily as with small numbers, and the occurrence of these numbers in the environment gives children experience of the need for them. Most real-life topics do not involve only mathematics, but are cross-curricular in nature. This, too, helps children to appreciate the relevance of both mathematics and other curriculum areas to real life.

Children in every age group can find mathematics in real life. The largest of the project schools has 21 classes. Very early in the project a six-year-old at that school asked her teacher: 'How many children are there in our school?' Instead of answering, the teacher sent her and a friend round the school to find out from each class how many children there were in that class. When they came back with their list of 21 classes, each containing 30 or more children, it was clear to the children that the calculator could help them to find the total. However, they had only had their calculators for about a week, and they had not yet discovered that the calculator could add more than two numbers at a time. The children's process for finding the total by adding the numbers two at a time was lengthy, but successful. The teacher could not have asked the children to find out the total for themselves if calculators had not been available. In addition to allowing the children to answer their own question, this activity gave them some feeling for the size of a number of more than 600, as they regularly saw hundreds of children in the hall, in the playgrounds and around the school.

A rather similar activity, where an even larger real-life number needed to be calculated, arose in a small rural school when the children were working on a project on the school and its environment. A group of eight and nine-year-olds set themselves the task of finding how many bricks had been used to build their (fortunately single-storied) school. They set off outside with a measuring tape, a calculator and a clipboard. They first walked round the school, and made a rough plan of the layout to help them to record the numbers of bricks used in each wall. They counted the number of bricks in a course (horizontal layer) of each wall and recorded this. They made several attempts to count the number of courses of bricks in each wall, but they found this difficult, as they could not reach to the top of the walls. They then decided to estimate the numbers of courses, and used the calculator to find an estimate of the total number of bricks in each wall. Some problems arose in adjusting the estimated total to take account of doors, windows and cavity walls. The children also considered the effect that errors in estimation might have on the final total. Later, they discussed their results with the rest of the class, and much debate ensued. Some issues raised were:

- The possible need for an accurate total instead of an estimated one: for instance, if the cost of bricks were important.

- Other possible ways of solving the problem.

- Ways of improving on estimated results.

In another village, a project was based on the village church. The children measured the church, drew plans and studied the patterns and symmetry in the architecture and decorations. One group decided to find how many people could be seated in the church. They measured the pews, and then needed to find how many people could be seated in a pew. Much measuring of sitting people led them to use averages. They also found that they needed to decide on the proportions of adults and children to be seated.

A class of eight to nine-year-olds investigated bicycles. Among other activities, some children studied the circumferences of wheels and worked out how far the bicycle travelled for one turn of the wheel. Others were fascinated by the gears. They found out about gear ratios and built working models of gears with different ratios. This involved a great deal of measurement and the use of angles.

A class of six and seven-year-olds were working on the topic of 'Transport'. Their work led them to investigate transport by car, rather than by bicycle. They started by looking at car number plates, organising traffic counts, and tallying how many cars of different colours passed the school. When the numbers became too large for mental calculation, the children reached for their calculators. Later, they investigated how members of staff got to school. Each teacher was asked how she or he travelled to school, how long it took, and the distance travelled. From this information, the children worked out how far each teacher travelled in a day, a week and a year. For instance, one teacher travelled four miles each way; one child calculated the weekly distance by doubling four mentally, and then entered $8 + 8 + 8 + 8 + 8 =$ on the calculator . Another child entered $5 \times 8 =$. The children then considered how many weeks in a year teachers went to school, and the distances travelled in a year. The children also found the amount of petrol the staff used in a week and in a year. Other calculations involved the price of petrol and the petrol consumption of different types of car. Staff transport had become a substantial resource for real-life mathematics.

Two teachers of seven and eight-year-olds worked together, in a team-teaching situation, to mount a topic on the 'Winter Olympics in 1988', which the children also followed avidly on television. The teachers' wide-ranging topic web contained elements from language, science, mathematics, CDT, environmental studies and other curriculum areas. Some important mathematical ideas emerged naturally, including these:

- As the temperatures were always below zero, negative numbers were inevitable, and the calculator became a teaching aid alongside a number-line extending below zero.

- The decimal point arose in lengths of jumps and the scoring in the skating competitions. The teachers found that any apprehensions or difficulties were in their own minds, rather than in the children's.

This topic involved much measurement. Some children were able to bring skis, boots and sticks to school, as well as ski clothes. These gave rise to a wide range of measuring activities, as did the events at the Olympic Games. Millimetres had to be used, as jumps were measured in thousandths of a metre. The children became very adept at estimating length. It was obvious that they had developed a real feeling for measures by the facility with which they selected and converted to the appropriate measure, even from metres to millimetres; 4 m was instantly converted to 4000 mm.

Sporting events such as the Olympic Games are often of great interest to children, as are their own athletic achievements. Most investigations of sport involve much mathematics, as the above account of the topic on the Winter Olympics shows.

Problems within mathematics itself

Children need to be able to use and apply the mathematics that they know, not only to real life, but also to problems within mathematics itself. These problems may have little application in real life, but children often find them fascinating. Because the mathematics does not have to be extracted from a real-life situation, problems within mathematics can help children to concentrate on developing problem-solving skills such as looking for patterns, tackling the work systematically, making conjectures about what will happen, and generalising from a few examples to make a general statement. These are important skills in all problem solving, and they develop slowly and as a result of much experience. Problems within mathematics may also lead children to mathematical content that is new to them.

A few examples are now given of problems within mathematics which children in the CAN project have tackled at various stages. In many classrooms, a great deal of mathematical investigation and exploration have taken place, and experience shows that children who investigate mathematics do develop their problem-solving skills.

A teacher of six to seven-year-olds asked children to investigate in how many ways they could arrange three different coloured pegs in a line. They then did the same for two pegs, and were very surprised that there were only two ways. Four pegs were much more difficult, and some children worked at random, so that they sometimes repeated themselves, or did not find all the different arrangements. However, one child had a systematic way of working, and was quite convinced that there could be no more arrangements. Some children's recording is shown in Figure 5.3, including that of the child who produced the 24 arrangements of four pegs in a systematic way. (Figure 5.3 has been annotated and keyed to show the original colour pattern.)

This teacher gave a list of her reasons for thinking that investigational work is important in CAN:

- No child has a wrong answer.
- Children always achieve something, no matter what their ability.
- In investigations, all the children can work at their own level.
- Some investigations provide opportunities to work in groups or pairs, providing collective discussion and collaboration.
- Some investigations lead to cross-curricular work.

However, there is a wide variation in the ages at which children become able to work systematically, as this description shows. Even the children who could not yet work systematically had a valuable experience, including the experience of hearing the convinced voice of the child who was certain there could be no more ways. It is the rightness of the mathematics that brings conviction.

Sometimes, an investigation leads children to new mathematical ideas. One teacher asked a group of seven to eight-year-olds to investigate a problem about a litre of orange juice:

> 'Suppose you start with a litre bottle of orange juice. You drink half on the first day, half of what is left the next day, and so on. How much juice will be left each day, and how long will the bottle last?'

The teacher wrote about how the children tackled the problem:

Bill laughed and said that you could go on for ever. However, he started to make a chart of how much would be left on each day. Andy set to work, hoping to find out how long the bottle would last. Phil at once saw him and said: 'You can go on for ever.' Other children said: 'Yes, but you can't really, because there wouldn't be enough orange juice to actually drink.'

The children then worked out how much liquid would be left each day. Some worked in fractions of a litre, and some worked in millilitres.

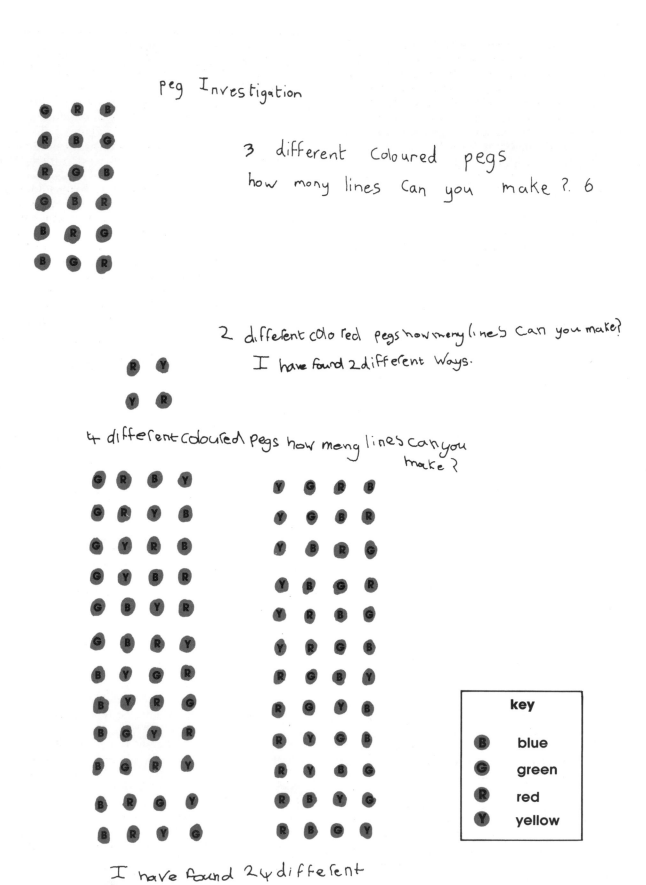

Peg Investigation

3 different Coloured pegs
how many lines Can you make ? 6

2 different colo red pegs how many lines Can you make?
I have found 2 different Ways.

4 different Coloured pegs how many lines can you make ?

I have found 24 different Ways

key

B   blue
G   green
R   red
Y   yellow

Figure 5.3

40

Hugh was working in millilitres. He found himself with 31¹/₄ ml, and he was trying to halve this. He told me it was hard, and I suggested that he use a calculator. He didn't, but he did change his fraction into a decimal. He explained what he was doing: 'Half of 30 is 15. Half of one is 0.5. A quarter is 0.25, so half of that is 0.12¹/₂.' I asked how we could put 0.12¹/₂ into a calculator. After discussion with me he decided it might be 0.125. So what was half of 31¹/₄? Hugh said: '15.5125,' but quickly corrected himself. 'Oh, no, 15.625.'

Tim said he had found halving 31¹/₄ quite easy! He said: 'Half of 30 is 15.' Then he said: 'A whole one is eight eighths and a quarter is two eighths, so I have got ten eighths, and a half of that is five eighths. So half of 31¹/₄ is 15⁵/₈.'

Tim's recording is shown in Figure 5.4. For the eighth day, he struggled to halve 15⁵/₈, abandoned it, and sensibly approximated the quantity on the ninth day as 4 ml.

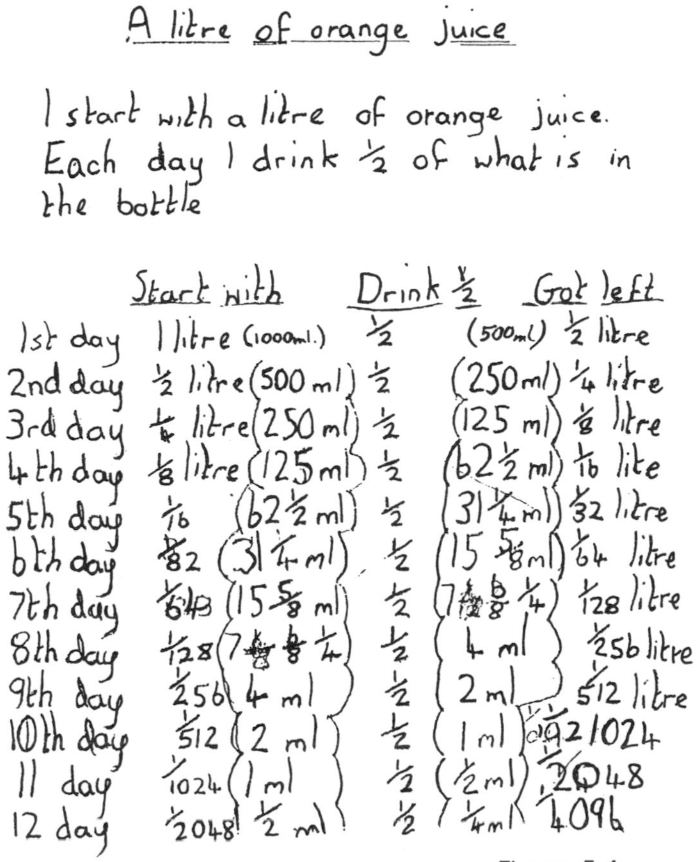

A litre of orange juice

I start with a litre of orange juice.
Each day I drink ½ of what is in the bottle

	Start with	Drink ½	Got left
1st day	1 litre (1000ml.)	½	(500ml) ½ litre
2nd day	½ litre (500 ml)	½	(250ml) ¼ litre
3rd day	¼ litre (250 ml)	½	(125 ml) ⅛ litre
4th day	⅛ litre (125ml)	½	(62½ ml) 1/16 lite
5th day	1/16 (62½ ml)	½	(31¼ ml) 1/32 litre
6th day	1/32 (31¼ ml)	½	(15⅝ ml) 1/64 litre
7th day	1/64 (15⅝ ml)	½	(7 [illegible] ¼) 1/128 litre
8th day	1/128 (7 [illegible] ¼)	½	(4 ml) 1/256 litre
9th day	1/256 (4 ml)	½	(2 ml) 1/512 litre
10th day	1/512 (2 ml)	½	(1 ml) 1/1024
11 day	1/1024 (1 ml)	½	(½ ml) 1/2048
12 day	1/2048 (½ ml)	½	(¼ ml) 1/4096

Figure 5.4

This problem enabled some of the children to strengthen their understanding of fractions and the connection between fractions and decimals. The idea that there is no limit to the smallness of numbers was also new to some children.

In another class, a group of eight to nine-year-olds carried out a number investigation from a workcard (Figure 5.5).

'Next to' number investigation

Make numbers by addition of consecutive numbers.
e.g. 3+4+5=12
6+7=13
Investigate.

Figure 5.5

Three children's accounts of their investigation are shown in Figures 5.6a, b, c. These children show different degrees of insight. Carrie and Rebecca have both seen that ***all odd numbers are sums of two consecutive numbers***, and Rebecca is able to explain why this happens. Only Carrie has seen the 'doubling' pattern in the impossible numbers, and Mandy is at an earlier stage, although she has realised that all odd numbers can be made. None of the children has explained ***why*** the numbers 2, 4, 8, 16, ... are impossible. The ability to prove rigorously that a conjecture must be correct develops much later than this in most children, although children will look for patterns and make conjectures at quite an early stage.

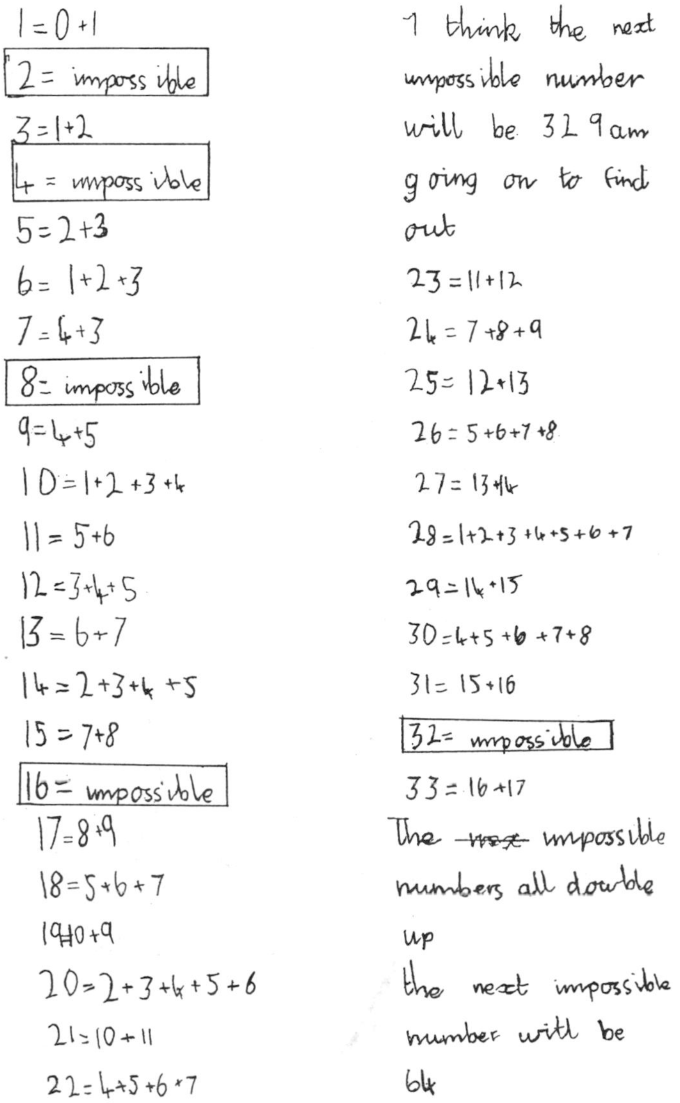

1=0+1
2= impossible
3=1+2
4 = impossible
5=2+3
6= 1+2+3
7=4+3
8= impossible
9=4+5
10=1+2+3+4
11=5+6
12=3+4+5
13=6+7
14=2+3+4+5
15=7+8
16= impossible
17=8+9
18=5+6+7
19=10+9
20=2+3+4+5+6
21=10+11
22=4+5+6+7

I think the next impossible number will be 32 I am going on to find out
23=11+12
24=7+8+9
25=12+13
26=5+6+7+8
27=13+14
28=1+2+3+4+5+6+7
29=14+15
30=4+5+6+7+8
31=15+16
32= impossible
33=16+17
The ~~next~~ impossible numbers all double up
the next impossible number will be 64

Figure 5.6a Carrie's account

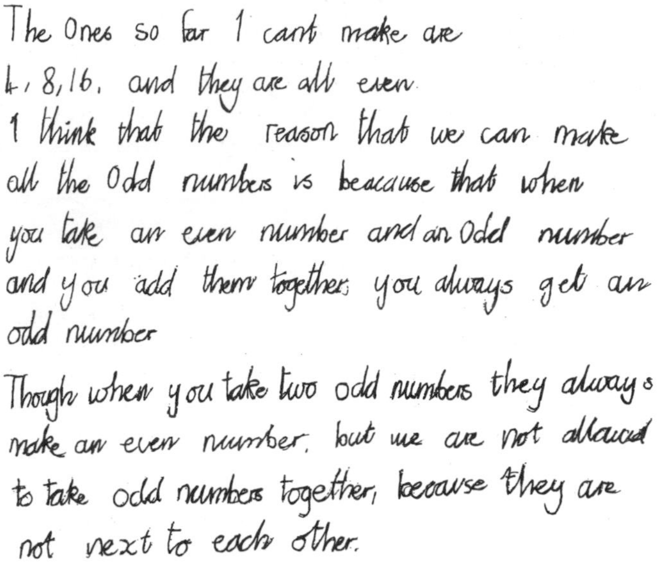

The Ones so far I can't make are 4, 8, 16, and they are all even.

I think that the reason that we can make all the Odd numbers is because that when you take an even number and an Odd number and you add them together, you always get an odd number

Though when you take two odd numbers they always make an even number, but we are not allowed to take odd numbers together, because they are not next to each other.

Figure 5.6b Rebecca's account

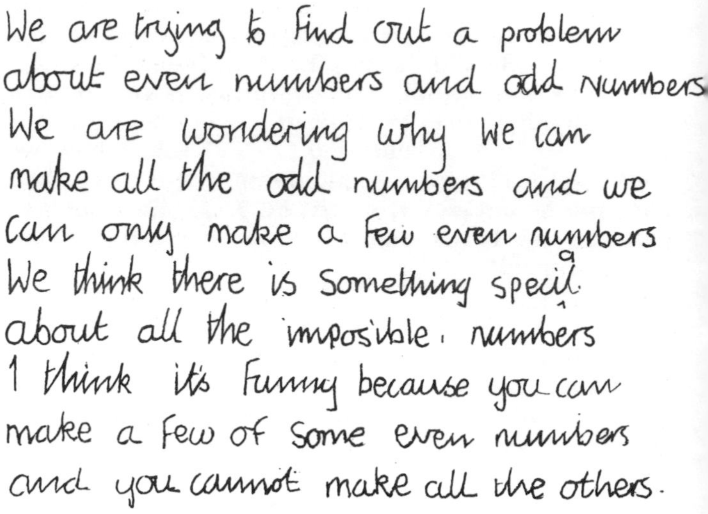

We are trying to find out a problem about even numbers and odd numbers. We are wondering why we can make all the odd numbers and we can only make a few even numbers. We think there is something special about all the impossible numbers. I think it's funny because you can make a few of some even numbers and you cannot make all the others.

Figure 5.6c Mandy's account

The next incident illustrates the variety of ways in which different children can approach the same mathematical problem, even within the same class. An advisory teacher had been working, over quite a long period, with a class of eight to nine-year-olds. The class teacher and the advisory teacher divided the class between them, and the advisory teacher worked for several sessions with the more able half of the class on the topic of 'Square Numbers'. To round off this work, he provided a workcard on which the children worked individually in the first half of the morning. After break, he gathered the group together to report back on what they had done. The reporting-back session was videotaped, so the children's contributions can be described in detail.

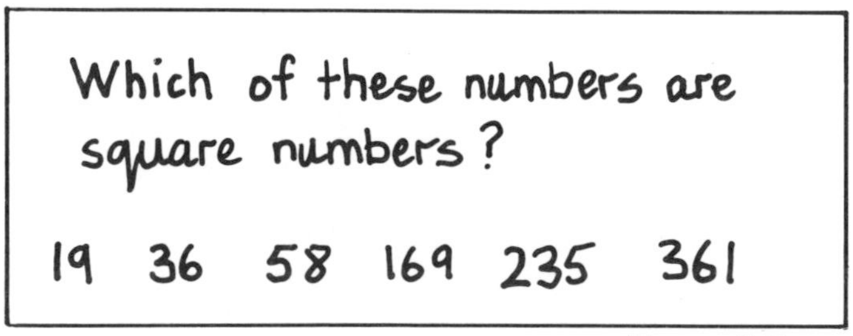

Which of these numbers are square numbers?

19   36   58   169   235   361

Figure 5.7

The workcard stated a problem (Figure 5.7). The teacher started by asking Jane, one of the least able in the group, how she had tackled it. Jane said she needed a list of square numbers, and so she had drawn some on squared paper and counted the squares. Her hands showed how she had counted a two-by-two square, a three-by-three square and a four-by-four square. Then she said: 'Then I realised that it was two rows of two, three rows of three, four rows of four. And so I could work the rest of the list out on the calculator.'

No doubt the teacher thought that Jane had realised some time ago how square numbers were calculated! The next child, Jason, also thought her method rather laborious. He said:

'You don't need to do all that. You know some square numbers. Like . . . I know 49 is a square number. And that's seven sevens. So the next square number is eight eights, which is 64. And 58 is between 49 and 64, so 58 can't be a square number.'

Susan then contributed:

'I made a list of square numbers, but I did it differently. I looked at the gaps. From 1 to 4, that's a gap of 3. From 4 to 9, that's a gap of 5. From 9 to 16, that's a gap of 7. And those gaps go up in twos. And it goes on like that, so you can build up the pattern from the gaps.'

Paula had taken a very different approach:

'I did it quite differently. I looked at the pattern of the unit figures. The unit figures go 1, 4, 9, 6 (in 16), 5 (in 25). And then it goes back again: 6 (in 36), 9 (in 49), 4 (in 64), 1 (in 81). And then you get 0 (in 100) which you haven't had before. And then the pattern starts again; 1 (in 121), 4 (in 144), and so it goes on. And there's never an 8 in that pattern, so 58 can't be a square number.'

This produced a thoughtful silence, as nobody else had thought of that idea, and they all needed to think it out. Finally, the teacher asked: 'Does anyone else want to say anything?' Gareth, who had not spoken before, took up the challenge:

'Yes. I do. I think you are all going in the wrong direction. You are only thinking about squares of whole numbers. In fact, every number is a square number. All you have to do is to put it into the calculator, and press that key, and it tells you what number it's the square of.'

'Oh', said the teacher, 'What key is that?' 'That one,' said Gareth. 'I don't know what it's called, but it tells you what number it's the square of.' The session concluded with the teacher introducing the group to the name and function of the **square root** key which Gareth had used.

Five children had revealed their methods. All were different and sensible. All the children showed awareness of mathematical pattern, and generalised from their first few examples. Jason and Paula were able to provide reasons for their assertions, and so were well on the way to having a concept of proof. Gareth was a real lateral thinker, able to ignore the assumption of the workcard that only some numbers were square numbers. His fresh approach led the teacher to introduce the new topic of square roots.

The examples in this chapter have shown how much children can gain in confidence, persistence and problem-solving skills when they are encouraged to use and apply their mathematics to a wide variety of problems and investigations. In many classes, this confident and autonomous approach to learning has also spread outside the bounds of mathematics, and teachers are encouraging children to use it in all their work.

6 THE DEVELOPMENT OF TEACHING

The project's style of working

CAN was part of the PrIME Project, and all PrIME's work was based on making use of the professional expertise of groups of teachers, who worked together to support one another in developing their thinking and their teaching. The CAN project worked in the same way as the rest of PrIME. The project team believed that the people who could best develop the curriculum for particular groups of children were the teachers who worked with those children every day, rather than 'experts' whose theoretical knowledge might be greater, but who were not in a position to respond each day to the children's developing thinking and understanding.

Of course, the teachers who worked in CAN needed to work together to support each other. A single teacher working alone finds it very difficult to innovate continuously with success. Support was provided by regular meetings of the teachers within each school, and regular cross-school meetings of the teachers in each LEA. The coordinator in the LEA and a member of the project team attended these meetings when possible; these people also provided support in the classroom when possible. Teachers also visited other schools. The project team wrote occasional discussion papers, shared useful ideas between groups, and organised conferences where teachers from different LEAs could meet one another and discuss their ideas.

The project team did not provide classroom activities for the teachers to use; nor did they tell the teachers how they should teach. CAN was based on the knowledge, enthusiasm and imagination of the teachers involved. It should be made clear that CAN was only part of the workload of the participating teachers, who continued to carry out the usual variety of work which all primary class teachers undertake. Similarly, CAN was only part of the workload of the support personnel, who were members of the PrIME project team, LEA advisory teachers and mathematics advisers.

Changing expectations

At the beginning of the project, the teachers found that they needed not only to continue in their familiar roles as teachers, but also to take on new roles as innovators and researchers. They needed to share their classroom experiences with one another, and they had to use their own and each others' ideas as starting points for innovation. There was no available research on the effects of the free use of calculators by young children, and nobody knew

what to expect. There were some available collections of calculator activities, but these were usually intended for older children, and were designed as additional activities to support the traditional curriculum.

At the start, most teachers felt insecure and confused about what they should do. The project team hoped that the teachers would be able to change the curriculum so that it would help the children's understanding of number to develop more strongly, and the children would be allowed free access to calculators. The children would not be taught the traditional methods of calculation. The teachers had to abandon their familiar ways of teaching the traditional vertical pencil-and-paper methods for addition, subtraction, multiplication and division. The fact that the teachers were not asked to change their teaching of other aspects of mathematics, such as shape, gave them little consolation. However, the teachers were urged to continue to provide practical activities to develop children's number concepts, as they had always done, and these activities gave the teachers some support as they started to think out new approaches.

At first, most teachers felt under pressure to invent structured classroom activities and to produce materials to introduce the calculator. However, many soon found that starting points gave the children a better stimulus than did structured activities. The children were able to take on these starting points and use them in their own way, choosing their own numbers, challenging themselves to extend as far as they could, and taking the activities in a variety of directions. A visitor asked one teacher how she was able to think of new activities. The teacher replied: 'Most of it comes from the children.' The visitor, who had a traditional background, did not understand the reply.

The teachers began to develop an exploratory and investigative style of working, which allowed the children freedom to take responsibility for their own learning. Topics for exploration took the place of practice exercises as the prevailing classroom activities. Because the number sections of the mathematics schemes used in the schools had been discarded, the teachers were able to move towards a different style of working. No longer did they have to 'cover' set topics in a set order. They began to notice that children's mathematics learning did not seem to progress in the ordered linear way in which it was traditionally structured. Individual children seemed to be putting together the network of mathematical concepts in their own individual ways. The differences between different children's mathematics were more fundamental than mere differences in speed of learning.

Children soon began to explore mathematical topics which the teachers had not expected, such as the negative numbers and decimals which they found on their calculators. Some teachers owned to a lack of expertise, and sought help from their colleagues. The expertise of all the teachers needed to be shared. One teacher wrote:

> **I feel at times that the children are far better mathematically minded than me and I feel a little inadequate to teach them.**

At first, the needed new approaches to the teaching of number caused the teachers anxiety, until they began to realise that the children were able to understand and use more mathematics than the teachers had expected. An infant teacher described how she had previously limited the children's work:

> **Prior to CAN, I tended to limit my teaching to numbers up to 20. I was therefore suprised to find a group of children counting confidently in hundreds when weighing objects using 100 gram weights.**

In fact, the greatest pressure on the teachers came from their anxiety to do the best for their pupils. This anxiety was alleviated when the teachers realised that, in CAN, the children seemed to enjoy mathematics more, and to know more mathematics than the teachers had expected.

The project did not take place in quiet isolation, but under the public gaze of many interested parties, and this also put pressure on the teachers. As the mathematics adviser in one particating LEA wrote about CAN:

> *It has addressed fundamental issues about learning and teaching mathematics in general, all of which has been done under the gaze of parents, governors, advisers, and educationalists in general.*
>
> [Durham County Council 1989]

However, the general interest in the project also became supportive to the teachers, who wished to share both their own developing ideas and the children's work with other teachers and with parents. Some of the teachers became active providers of INSET about CAN and other topics within their LEAs, and in some schools meetings for parents flourished.

Styles of teaching

Teachers began to realise that small changes, or in some cases quite dramatic changes, were taking place in their approach to teaching mathematics. Usually their teaching styles changed gradually and slowly as the teachers rethought their views about mathematics teaching. The teachers began to *listen* more carefully to what children said, and they encouraged children to *talk* more about mathematics. Teachers set up 'discussion time' in mathematics, and found this very valuable, particularly in assessing children's understanding. Many teachers encouraged the children to discuss their approaches to particular tasks and problems, and their methods of non-calculator calculation. In these discussions the teachers showed that they valued the variety of the children's approaches, and they helped children to see that other peoples' methods were also valid. A teacher described the relationship between the children's methods and the teacher's ideas:

> **Although the teacher may occasionally offer a method or pathway, the children will still devise their own methods.**

Teachers found that they appreciated children's individual ways of tackling mathematical tasks, and they were praising them, rather than suggesting that a child had done something 'the wrong way'.

Teachers discovered that their planning for mathematics now needed to be much more open ended, and they had to be prepared for unexpected results. When something unexpected happened, teachers had to be ready to share their surprise with the children, to explore with them and to learn alongside them. The teacher became much more a *participator* and a *motivator*, rather than an instructor. A teacher summed up this change in her role:

> **The project has brought about changes in teaching styles. It has shown the need for flexibility, thinking on one's feet, seizing the opportunities as they arise and learning to make the most of the leads children give us.**

Another teacher described her perception that the changes were fundamental to her whole teaching role:

> **Role reversal is the best description of my rethinking. I gradually became an adviser and listener rather than an instructor. I became the learner, the children the teachers. My mind was opened to new approaches, new ideas, new concepts. I began to realise that my way was not necessarily the only correct way.**

The project's evaluator summed up the teachers' new attitudes, and commented on their enjoyment of the changes:

> **They appreciate the new role – no longer are they the sole providers of mathematical activity. Children are given an opportunity to follow ideas associated with their own experiences and to devise their own methods of recording. Teachers stand back and listen, intervening only to stimulate mathematical thinking.**

Changes in classroom organisation followed from the teacher's development into a participator and motivator. The classroom needed to be re-organised to allow the children enough space in which to work, and to give them access to all the apparatus and materials that they might need. The children's own wishes in these matters also became more important than before:

> I needed to think about the children's ideas about where things should be stored, and where they were happy working. How much space did they need? How available was the apparatus to them? Were all the necessary tools available – bricks, counters, Multi-link, calculators, coloured pens, paper, duplicating facilities, etc, etc?

Different teachers used different strategies to incorporate mathematics within the whole year's programme of work. Some teachers continued to set aside identifiable times during the day when children did mathematics. Others placed most of the mathematics, as well as other curriculum areas, within cross-curricular topic work. A member of the project team, on one tour of visits to classrooms in a particular area, saw no 'mathematics lessons' at all. However, a great deal of valuable mathematics was taking place in the cross-curricular topics which were being explored in all the classrooms.

As teachers found their way through to new styles of mathematics teaching, they usually decided that, although it was hard work, the CAN style of teaching was a more enjoyable and exciting experience than mathematics had previously been. One teacher, in looking back on her own professional development, emphasised her growing confidence:

> Through developing activities, considering children's responses, and placing a greater emphasis on listening and talking with children and trying to understand how they think mathematically, I feel more confident in teaching mathematics.

An infant teacher, who was involved in CAN throughout the first three years, and who was nearing retirement, looked back on three years' work:

> Initially, I was very enthusiastic and excited at the prospect. The reason was that I had always felt that there must be better ways of interesting young children in numbers than those I had previously practised throughout 30 or so years of teaching mathematics to very young children.

> After the initial euphoria, my thoughts were mixed. Perhaps I might have an opportunity to ease some of the difficulties and dislikes that some children associate with number. My own experiences of number work all my school life had been, to say the least, horrific. Could I grasp this opportunity fully, and perhaps make mathematics something to be enjoyed into adult life? Conversely, I was treading unknown ground, and was sometimes overcome with panic. Would I waste time, would I be able to keep their enthusiasm, could I persuade them to abandon their rows of algorithms for a more logical reasoning and understanding approach?

> Now, three school years on, after a lot of hard work, many self-doubts, many panics and many hours of concentrated thought processes, the children and myself have won through to a freedom and familiarity with numbers that I would not have believed possible. The joy and pleasure gained from our CAN maths for us all is superb, and a marvellous gift to me in my last teaching years.

> I don't really understand how it worked for my class and me. We were explorers in a new world of adventure amongst numbers, we trod many new roads, went into unknown territory, along many unexplored paths; sometimes we found it hard going, sometimes we lost our way, but the end result was a wonderful rewarding experience that I hope the children will never forget.

> I was rewarded by developing a love of numbers that I never had in all my school days; my children opened up a veritable treasure chest for me, and I hope I gave them a key to open a door into their future world of number work. Mathematics for them will, I hope, be remembered as fun, excitement, fulfilment and success.

As the teachers changed their styles of teaching mathematics, it is not surprising that their new ideas affected many other things, both in their classrooms and in the school. At first, some teachers found that they were doing an increased amount of number work, but perhaps they were neglecting other aspects of mathematics such as weight, length, time, capacity and shape. However, this neglect corrected itself later, as a CAN approach to teaching spread first to other parts of mathematics, and then to other curriculum areas. The project's style of working through sharing, support and collaboration between teachers also encouraged teachers to work together in other curriculum areas, and in other aspects of school life:

> Aspects of CAN teaching styles have flowed into other areas of the curriculum.

> The teacher development model is affecting the rest of the staff.

It became increasingly clear to the teachers that, as an adviser wrote:

> The project as it has evolved has not just been about calculators.

Indeed, in many schools the project has not been just about mathematics.

Support from teachers' meetings

The teachers deserved a great deal of support as they began to work on CAN. They were tackling a very difficult task of innovation in an area of mathematical education – the use of calculators by young children – in which very little work had previously been done anywhere in the world. It was also an innovation of which some members of the public were expected to be very critical, and this caused some initial anxieties.

The project was not able to provide as much support as the teachers deserved. However, by working together and supporting one another, and by making good use of such support as the LEA and the project team were able to provide, the teachers rose magnificently to the challenge. It is a tribute to the success of their innovation that, although CAN has not been totally incorporated into the National Curriculum in mathematics, both the Attainment Targets and *Mathematics: Non-Statutory Guidance* expect that children will use calculators from Key Stage 1 onwards.

The teachers found that a major source of support was the teachers' meetings at which CAN was discussed. As one teacher wrote:

> I think a very important factor in my own development has been not only the involvement with the children, but with colleagues on a regular basis, where we ourselves practise talking about it, thus helping our own understanding and clarity.

At first, only a few teachers in each school were personally involved in the project, and meetings for all the teachers in an LEA were sometimes found more supportive than meetings within a single school. However, as time went on, more and more teachers in each school were involved, and it became clear that CAN was developing into a whole-school enterprise, on which all the teachers in the school needed to work together.

At teachers' meetings, ideas and activities were shared, and time could be set aside for teachers to work with one another to devise activities. Teachers described work which their children had done, and were often surprised at the children's determination, understanding and imagination. For example, at one meeting a teacher described a five-year-old's counting of her collection of 80 marbles, which she had done by grouping the marbles in tens. The child had done this activity by her own choice, and she had recorded it both in drawing and in writing. All the teachers were surprised that the child could cope confidently with such large numbers, and could write them without help. Experiences such as this caused the teachers to do a great deal of questioning and rethinking of their approaches; they developed their own thinking about mathematics learning, and their expectations of the children grew. The meetings gave the teachers themselves opportunities to learn in the type of CAN environment that they were trying to produce in their own classrooms. Contributions came from young and older teachers, from experienced and inexperienced teachers. Those involved in the project included teachers in their first appointment, and teachers nearing retirement.

Sometimes, the same difficulties and concerns arose at teachers' meetings in different areas. Teachers were often anxious about the best ways of keeping records of each child's growing understanding. They were also anxious about how they might best help children who asked 'difficult' questions about the negative numbers and decimal numbers which were shown on the calculator display. There could not be set answers to these mathematical questions; they were a new experience for all the teachers, and much more experience would be needed before teachers felt confident in handling them. Teachers were also sometimes anxious about the fact that children were recording their mathematics in ways which were very different from the traditional methods of recording. However, the teachers were heartened by the fact that this recording, and the thinking on which it was based, was certainly the children's own; the individuality of the children's recording gave the teachers insights into the children's thinking.

Working with colleagues in the project was an important INSET experience for the teachers, as the support of others enabled them to broaden their thinking and develop their teaching. A mathematics adviser wrote about this INSET aspect of the project:

> *The INSET value of involvement in the project to teachers, schools and the Authority has been significant. This has resulted from the project structure. Teachers have been working on an important issue in the classroom with their own class.* [Durham County Council 1989]

Support from the headteacher

In every school, the headteacher played a crucial part in the development of CAN. At the beginning of the project, it was the headteacher who was the active representative of the school, engaged in bringing about the school's involvement in CAN. Lengthy discussions with the LEA mathematics adviser were needed, together with detailed consultations with the staff of the school. Before putting the school's name forward to the LEA, the headteacher needed to make a realistic assessment of the school's capability for continued innovation over a long period of time.

Once the project was under way, it was the responsibility of the headteacher to present the public face of CAN to the outside world. The headteacher often had to discuss the rationale for the project, and its progress, with groups of parents. Individual parents might also discuss with the headteacher their concerns about their children's progress, and the differences between CAN and the traditional curriculum. The headteacher needed to seek support from the school's governors, and they needed to be regularly informed about the project's progress. Visitors descended on the schools from near and far. Teachers came from other primary schools, curious to see the style of mathematics teaching used in CAN, and to find out how young children used calculators. Teachers from the next phase of education came to see what was happening to pupils whom they would receive later. Other visitors included HMI and LEA advisers, student teachers and their tutors, and visiting educators from abroad. The headteacher was the initial contact for all these visitors, and the focus of their queries and their requests for explanations. However, by the time that CAN had begun to attract large numbers of visitors, the headteachers were strengthened in their commitment by the growing confidence and enthusiasm of both teachers and children.

Throughout the project, the headteachers led and supported their staffs in many ways which were essential to the success of the project. Headteachers often worked alongside teachers in the classroom, sharing with the class teacher the task of discussing mathematics with the children and stimulating their investigations. Often, headteachers took classes in order that members of staff could attend teachers' meetings in school time. Headteachers needed to involve themselves closely in the detailed discussions about mathematics that were taking place in their schools, so that they could provide both support and leadership for their staffs.

Many teachers commented on the value of the support they received from the headteacher, emphasising that without it, they would not have been able to continue. Headteachers were also closely involved with their staffs in developing record-keeping systems, and they often helped teachers to assess children's progress.

As time went on, it continued to be important for the headteacher to make on-going assessments of the school's needs, so that problems could be anticipated and forestalled. One headteacher looked back regretfully at errors in the organisation of teachers' meetings, made early in the project:

In retrospect, it is now obvious that, for the success of the project to be maintained and consolidated, a greater proportion of the time should have been spent working with *all* staff members, in order to give confidence and support to every teacher.

The same headteacher listed some of the many areas of concern which, in CAN, required regular and time-consuming attention from the head:

Other issues to be addressed are liaison with secondary schools, the support of parents, the demands of the National Curriculum, the role of the school's maths scheme, and integration of CAN into the school's cross-curricular thematic approach.

In truth, without the commitment of the headteachers, the CAN project would have been unlikely to make much progress.

Support from advisory teachers

Advisory teachers are teachers who are appointed by an LEA, not to the staff of a particular school, but with the task of visiting a number of schools. They provide support for teachers, both by working alongside them in the classroom and by discussing ideas and difficulties with individual teachers and with groups of teachers. The CAN project was very fortunate that its timing coincided with a period when central government funding supported the appointment, by each LEA, of several advisory

teachers in primary mathematics. These teachers were experienced primary teachers who had a special interest and expertise in mathematics. Often, an advisory teacher was the LEA coordinator for CAN, and other advisory teachers also took part in the work, in LEAs and in schools.

Advisory teachers were a lifeline for many teachers at the beginning of the project, and an on-going support throughout its lifetime. Advisory teachers helped to organise and plan teachers' meetings, and to develop appropriate children's activities. Most importantly, advisory teachers worked alongside teachers in their classrooms, and they were always willing to talk with teachers about their successes, worries and difficulties.

Many teachers commented on the value of their classroom support. One teacher, looking back at her first year of CAN, described the help she had received from an advisory teacher:

CAN has enabled me to be involved in a whole new way of approaching maths. Previous to this I had always worked in ability groups and had always allowed children plenty of practical work before recording. Since the advisory teacher has been coming into my class, this policy has been taken a step further and my role has changed from teaching to learning with the children – allowing the children to discover answers for themselves. I now allow more time for discussion and for children to listen to one another. I really appreciate the help and support I have received, and have certainly benefited from it.

A headteacher also described the valuable support the school had received from an advisory teacher:

Credit must be given to the advisory teacher for her planning of programmes, following up information, constructive help and most of all for her physical involvement with the children. On behalf of the school I should like to thank her for all her hard work and support during her visits.

Another headteacher attributed a great deal of the success of the project to the advisory teacher:

The success of this project has been due to the work of the advisory teacher who travels from school to school, and to the meetings held at the teachers' centre.

These headteachers did not at all exaggerate the value of the advisory teachers' work in CAN. Not only did the advisory teachers provide a link between the schools, carrying ideas and activities from one school to another. More importantly, they provided an example, in the classroom, of ways in which the class teacher could develop a new style of working with children in mathematics.

Changes in personnel

As the first cohort of children grew older, and as later year-groups of children joined the project, additional teachers were involved in CAN. At the end of each year of the project, some groups of children transferred from infant schools to junior schools, or from first schools to middle schools, and teachers in these new schools became involved.

It became clear that it was important to involve new teachers in the work before they received a project class. New teachers were encouraged to visit project classrooms and to attend teachers' meetings and national conferences. However, the usual flow of teachers changing posts made some last minute staff changes inevitable. Consequently, some children who had been involved in CAN for a year or more moved to the classes of teachers who had only just begun to think about CAN. Many of these teachers were apprehensive at first, and found the children's approaches difficult to cope with. Sometimes, when the teacher was new to CAN, the children's mathematics learning seemed to stand still for a time, while the teacher adjusted to the new approach. However, it is difficult to know whether children usually stand still while they adjust to a different teacher's way of working. One teacher identified problems in consulting more experienced colleagues:

▐ **When a new teacher comes into a 'second year of CAN' class, is it a benefit having an experienced teacher to turn to in the school, or is it threatening to the beginner?** ▐

In the first year of the project, the teachers and the children were all new to CAN. In later years, some teachers received new classes of six and seven-year-olds and started CAN again. One teacher described the children's problems in adjusting to a new approach:

▐ **In CAN, a new class seems 'slow to start', whereas in the first year we learnt together.** ▐

As time went on, it became clear that a whole-school commitment to CAN was necessary. Developing this commitment was a long-term process, and was very demanding of teachers' time and energy. Inevitably, different teachers had different educational views, and staff changes also affected the development of a whole-school philosophy. Some teachers were initially sceptical about the wisdom of using calculators with young children; a few teachers had a strong conviction that children needed to learn the traditional pencil-and-paper vertical methods of calculation. However, as the project progressed and teachers saw what the children were able to do, attitudes changed. As the staff of a school supported one another in their rethinking, the teachers' confidence grew and their approaches to mathematics teaching developed.

In a few schools, there was a change of headteacher during the project. One headteacher has written about this experience. His school was in CAN from the beginning, and he was committed to its development. However, changes of headship in one or two nearby project schools caused him to reflect on the problems:

▐ **Inevitably, there will sometimes be new headteachers in schools where CAN is running. I think this is an extremely difficult task. To come to a headship is hard enough. On top of this you are expected to support and continue a revolutionary piece of curriculum development, despite not having the kind of ownership and understanding which will be possessed by members of your staff who are involved. You may also have to deal with other members of staff (or parents or governors) who are not convinced, and who see your arrival as the chance they are waiting for.** ▐

This head was a teaching head, but his class was not involved at the beginning of the project. He went on:

▐ **Once I was teaching a project class, the doubts and worries were replaced by conviction and enthusiasm, so that I was able to be a much more convincing advocate. I was fortunate that I was a teaching head. For a head of a large school, coming in from outside and taking over a project school, it would be much harder.** ▐

Fortunately, few schools had changes of headteacher during the project.

7 LIAISON AND COMMUNICATION

Liaison with parents and governors

Some educational issues reach out beyond classrooms and teachers, and are the subject of general public debate. For teachers who are involved in curriculum development, these issues may have an impact on the effectiveness of their work. This was certainly true for the teachers who worked on CAN.

One such issue was the involvement of parents and governors. The project schools all realised that parents play a major part in their children's learning; when parents are actively involved, their enthusiasm encourages and helps their children. On the other hand, if children feel that their parents are unhappy with the school, the children find themselves in a conflict situation which can inhibit learning.

Mathematics and reading are particularly vulnerable to pressures such as these. Some schools which worked on CAN had previously taken part in schemes for parental involvement in children's reading. These schools quickly and confidently began to share with parents the ways in which they were starting to work on CAN. Other schools were more apprehensive, and were concerned about 'what the parents will say' about the use of calculators. Some schools felt that working with parents in mathematics would not be similar to involvement in home-reading schemes. Most schools can assume that parents have a reasonable facility in reading, but this might not be the case in mathematics. Some schools also thought that parents might have entrenched ideas about the teaching of mathematics, especially the teaching of numbers. Nevertheless, all the project schools recognised the importance of parental support, and made determined efforts to overcome any difficulties. As one headteacher commented: 'Schools push ahead with innovation at their peril if they ignore parents or governors.'

Great efforts were made, not only to keep individual parents informed about their own child's mathematics, but also to ensure that all parents knew about the aims of the project. Schools reported that when parents became convinced, they were then powerful advocates for CAN to other parents. One parent was heard to say:

❡ I wish maths had been like this when our older children were this age. I hadn't realised how little thought it takes to do a page of sums. This is much more challenging. ❡

It became clear that all the teachers in a school needed to work together to achieve a good parent–school partnership. When teachers talked with parents about mathematics, it was essential that all the teachers should give the same message about the aims of CAN.

The other groups which played an important part in supporting CAN were the governing bodies of the schools. The school governors needed to be informed about the project and involved in its work. Sometimes, a member of the project team was invited to attend a governors' meeting. Sometimes, the headteacher or a member of staff would speak at a meeting. Parent governors often provided a link with other groups, enabling fruitful discussions to take place at governors' meetings. In addition, many governors visited classrooms to see the project at first hand, and talked to the teachers and the children.

Ways of working with parents

All the schools informed the parents about the project before it began, either by inviting them to meetings or by writing to them. Preliminary information to parents usually focused on the fact that the children would use calculators. At meetings, however, the aims of the project could be explained, and parents' fears, such as worries about possible 'mindless button pressing', could be explored. One school had previously organised a project to involve parents in mathematics, and this gave the teachers confidence in approaching parents.

Some schools held parents' meetings and workshops at termly intervals during the project. These meetings often included hands-on calculator activities, and teachers found that they were very productive in enlisting parental support. Even at the start, only a few parents seemed apprehensive, or were overtly critical of CAN. The great majority were willing to trust the school's judgement; indeed, they were often enthusiastic about the opportunity given to their children. One teacher reported that at the first open evening, all the parents who attended (26 out of a possible 29) were very positive about CAN. Many of these parents bought calculators for their children, and actively encouraged their use at home.

Meetings for parents also offered opportunities for informal discussion with individual parents, so that questions and concerns could be raised. Soon, schools reported that parents were showing an increased interest in the project, and in mathematics education generally. As the project went on, many parents told the teachers that their children were now approaching mathematics with greater confidence and enthusiasm. As one teacher commented: 'The children have been our greatest ambassadors.'

Some parents expressed concern that they could no longer help with their children's mathematics. This brought out the importance of regular workshops, which could help parents to understand what their children were doing at that time.

In the later years of the project, schools needed to set up meetings and workshops for parents of new cohorts of children. These parents were able to look at examples of previous children's work, and they could be shown how the calculator assisted children in learning mathematics. One parent sent the following apology for absence from a meeting for parents of children new to CAN:

> Unfortunately, I am unable to come to the meeting this evening due to previous arrangements. As you know I already have Jane on the project and Margaret is now joining in. I think I am probably one of the only parents with two children on the project. As you know I fully support this scheme and should any new parents want a chat with me about how I think Jane has benefited from this I would only be too happy to do so. Keep up the good work.

By demonstrating their approval of CAN, parents also provided support for the teachers. One new teacher was anxious about how she could justify the work to parents, when she herself was not yet fully convinced. She found to her great surprise that the parents explained to her their reasons for being so happy with the new curriculum.

Another approach was to invite parents into the classroom. In one school, throughout the project, parents worked on mathematical activities with children in the classroom. The calculator became an accepted tool for these parents, and they were able to see at first hand how its use supported children's understanding of number, and how it encouraged the development of mental calculation.

As expected, a minority of parents remained unconvinced, and would have preferred a more formal teaching approach. Some were unhappy with the children's methods of recording; some wanted to see more evidence of their children's knowledge of the multiplication facts. Many parents wanted reassurance that their children would not lose out when they moved to the next school. Some schools invited the LEA mathematics adviser to meetings to discuss these issues with parents. However, a very small number of parents remained unconvinced.

Because of the need for parental involvement, all the teachers had to be able to justify CAN, and to provide convincing answers to questions such as these:

- Won't they come to rely on the calculator, making them lazy in mental arithmetic?
- If this is as advanced as you say, what happens when our child transfers to another primary or secondary school?
- What will happen when these children have to sit public examinations?
- Will they still learn their tables?
- When will they learn the normal ways of adding up and taking away?
- Will they learn to write down their sums in a tidy way?
- Tell me more about mental calculation.
- How can you be sure this will work and our children are not just guinea pigs?
- My child is always telling me she plays lots of games in maths – that doesn't seem right.
- What can I do to help at home?

The teachers demonstrated a growing ability to convince parents by discussion and example. This was also very valuable for the teachers' professional development; it encouraged them to question their own practice, and it often strengthened their understanding of mathematics and their commitment to CAN. Their growing conviction and knowledge also enabled the teachers to retain the support of the great majority of parents.

Working with parents and governors: some ideas

All the schools developed their own ways of working with parents and governors, and ideas were often discussed at teachers' meetings in the LEAs. As a result of the sharing of ideas between schools, one group of teachers drew up a list (displayed on page 52) of tried and tested ways of encouraging the involvement of parents and governors.

Another group of teachers gave this advice to those who were planning a parents' meeting:

> Don't forget, if it doesn't come up, look around and say with a smile: 'Aren't you going to ask about tables?'

Transfer to the next school

The project had been in existence for only a year when the first children transferred to new schools; in September 1987 some children in the project's first cohort moved from infant schools to junior schools. In 1988 some children moved from five-to-eight first schools to eight-to-twelve middle schools, and in 1989 some children moved from five-to-nine first schools to nine-to-thirteen middle schools. Thus, the project already has a good deal of experience of transfer to the next school. The first transfers of eleven-year-old children to secondary schools was due to take place in 1991.

When a group of children transfers to the next school, they may have to adapt to many changes, both in the

```
YOU COULD...........

* Invite parents and governors to an evening meeting
to explain the CAN curriculum philosophy and give an
opportunity for discussion of the issues raised.
Following one such meeting, one group of parents
asked for a termly meeting to discuss progress and
raise issues.

* Get teachers who have experience of working on CAN
to talk to your parents and governors. The
enthusiasm of those already working on CAN is
valuable, and can support teachers who have yet to
embark on CAN.

* Talk to your local high/middle/upper/secondary
school mathematics department. Get them to visit
your school, and to come to your meetings with
parents and governors. When parents say 'What about
when they go to the next school?' or 'What about
GCSE?', the staff of the secondary school can
respond. Much preparation will be needed to ensure
that the secondary school staff have a good
understanding of CAN, and that they do support your
aims.

* Hold evening workshops, offering calculator
activities for children. Parents and governors can
watch and listen or have a go themselves. Try to
encourage them to do something themselves - but
stress that listening is very important at first.
Give parents an opportunity for discussion with
staff.

* Open up your school one morning or afternoon for
parents and governors to come in to watch and get
involved in mathematical activities. The children
are your best ambassadors! You could open the school
regularly on one day a week, or vary the day so as
not to exclude those parents who have regular
commitments such as playgroups.

* Buy calculators through the county suppliers. At
your first meeting, sell them to parents for their
children. (Check that this is 'legal'!) Children
like to have their own machines, and they will
continue activities at home. Encourage this and make
it clear to parents that this is very helpful for
their children.

* Provide a sheet of ideas that children can do at
home. Sometimes you can send home activities that
the whole family can enjoy. Provide a sheet for
parents to write their comments about the activity,
and their suggestions for its improvement!

* Send home a questionnaire asking parents to detail
their own use of mathematics, and of calculators.
Ask them to outline their attitude to the use of
calculators in school.

FINALLY...........

Be prepared for legitimate queries, and for natural
worries and reservations. One teacher group suggests
that if parents and governors do not raise sensitive
issues, you should do so yourself; this brings
things into the open and demonstrates both your
awareness of the issues and your confidence in CAN.
```

Before each transfer took place, some teachers from the receiving school visited the previous school to see the children in their classrooms, and to discuss the project with the class teachers. One school gave the receiving school folders containing examples of each child's work. These folders showed the types of activity to which the children were accustomed, and indicated the level of work of which each child was capable. Some groups of teachers invited middle or secondary school colleagues to attend teachers' meetings and workshops, and encouraged them to visit displays of children's work.

Transfer to the next school did sometimes cause difficulties. In these cases, the headteachers usually consulted together about the problems, and liaison between the two schools developed as the teachers exchanged ideas. The first transfers showed the importance of effective and early communication. It also became clear that it takes time for a receiving school to accept the CAN philosophy, and to adapt its day-to-day working to the new situation. Even within the same school, new teachers often take some time to adjust to CAN; it is even more difficult for teachers in another school to adjust, when they cannot consult daily with experienced colleagues in the same school. One recurring problem is that receiving schools often have several feeder schools, and may have to place children who have worked on CAN in the same classes as children who have worked in other ways.

Liaison with secondary schools was first considered in the second year of the project. In one primary school, the head's anxieties were alleviated when the head of the receiving secondary school visited the primary school and said that he was happy with the school's way of working. Subsequent visits by mathematics teachers from the secondary school were very successful. In another area, each member of the secondary school mathematics department visited the primary school for half a day, to talk with the teachers and to observe the mathematics. Although the primary teachers were rather nervous before these visits, they were uplifted by the positive enthusiasm and support of the secondary teachers. The head of the secondary mathematics department wrote to the primary head after the visits:

The work being done under the auspices of the CAN project was open-ended and challenging. As secondary school teachers, we feel that the work being done by the pupils encourages us to be demanding of them when they reach us. We are ourselves trying to integrate a more investigative approach to the teaching and learning of mathematics.

Other secondary teachers who visited feeder schools also commented in a positive way:

The children are working the way we want for GCSE.

The children don't seem to be disconcerted by getting wrong answers in the way they do by traditional crosses in exercise books. Instead they look for what went wrong and often correct it.

general ethos of the school and in its organisation. Positive efforts are needed to make sure that the progress of the children's learning is not affected by these changes. It was expected that, in CAN, some difficulties might arise from a more formal approach to teaching in the receiving schools than that in the infant or first schools from which the children came.

We were amazed at the children's ability to do running totals in their head.

One child I noticed had better keyboard competence with the calculator than secondary pupils doing GCSE this year. ▰

It seems that some middle and secondary schools can readily accept the challenge of CAN, but other schools will find it more difficult to adjust. Schools that find adjustment difficult may use more formal teaching approaches, and teachers may have fixed expectations about how mathematics should be recorded and presented. The teachers may also believe in a transmission model of teaching mathematics, and not encourage children to think in their own individual ways. Children who have worked in the CAN project have had little previous experience of these attitudes to mathematics teaching, and they may experience confusion and discouragement.

It is very important that the teachers in receiving schools should be well briefed about the work that the children have done, and the ways in which they are accustomed to working; this will enable the children's understanding to be successfully built on by the receiving school. However, transfer is most successful when receiving schools and teachers are involved in the project well in advance, and when they are given support and encouragement while they work out their own ways of continuing to apply the CAN philosophy in the new school.

Children who transfer into project classes

During the project, a number of children have transferred to project schools, and have found themselves in classes which had been working on CAN for some time. Other children have moved out of project schools. These transfers have usually been caused by family moves, but the reasons for a few moves related to CAN. A few children were transferred by the parents to schools which used a more formal approach, although the children were achieving well in CAN. Other children were transferred by their parents to schools which were involved in CAN.

Some children who transferred to project classes did so without problems, but others were less successful. Much depended on the styles of teaching which the child had previously experienced. The children who had problems were those who entered CAN from very structured and directed classrooms, in which mathematics was usually tightly based on published schemes. The teachers who received these children tried gradually to accustom them to the CAN approach. However, some children suffered a loss of confidence and a sense of helplessness.

Lack of confidence and helplessness may have arisen because the children were asked to carry out activities which were nothing like their previous experience of

mathematics. To some extent, the difficulty depended on the length of time for which the child's new class had been working on CAN; some children may have been thrown in at the deep end in an experienced project class. Insufficient attention may at first have been paid to their particular needs, because the problem was a new one to the teacher.

Some new children were 'good at sums' and could perform calculations successfully if told what to do. It must have seemed to them that there were no longer any 'proper mathematics lessons'. New children also had to work in situations where the other members of the class were active, independent, confident and enthusiastic learners, who used a range of informal methods and made use of the calculator whenever they chose. It is no wonder that some children felt inadequate and displayed defensive behaviour. Their parents, who were still unfamiliar with CAN, may also have given them negative messages.

Teachers who received these children developed a variety of ways of supporting them. One group of teachers pooled their experience to draw up the following advice:

- Make an assessment, by observation and discussion, of what a child can do with materials or techniques which are familiar.

- Give reassurance that the child's ideas are still valid in the new classroom, and use a more directive teaching approach with the child.

- Boost confidence by asking the child to show others one of the standard pencil-and-paper methods of calculation. Ask other children to share their own methods of calculation with the new child.

- Identify activities in which other children can work alongside the new child, but which are accessible to the new child's way of working.

- Identify and build on the strengths of the child's way of working. Encourage attributes such as persistence, an enquiring mind, an acceptance of a range of answers, enjoyment, perseverance, the use of problem-solving strategies, and a collaborative approach to learning.

However, although the teachers worked very hard to support children who were new to the project, some children did take quite a long time to settle to a way of working which they had not previously experienced.

Visitors to the project schools

Communication and liaison with visitors to the schools were also necessary. All the project schools received many visitors. The increasing numbers of visitors demonstrate the widespread interest in the project. Visitors included teachers from primary and secondary schools throughout Britain, educators from overseas, HMI, advisory staff, and teacher education lecturers and student teachers.

The schools were always very willing to show visitors the project classes at work, but sometimes the sheer numbers of visitors had a disruptive effect on the children's work. In one extreme case, a child was asked by his teacher: 'What have you done today?' He replied: 'I've talked to 17 visitors.' This surfeit of visitors forced some schools to stop receiving visitors for a time. Other schools moved to a pattern of one visiting day each week; they worked with other schools in the LEA to ensure that visitors could see a project school on most days of the week.

Many children coped very well with the stream of visitors; they became confident and articulate in explaining to adults what they were doing, and they readily involved visitors in their activities. The children's powers of communicating mathematics grew rapidly, and they enjoyed the interest which the visitors showed in their work.

One problem was the variety of the visitors' perceptions of CAN. In some cases, visitors' expectations of classroom practice led to difficulties; the visitor did not appreciate the teacher's role in the project classroom or understand the CAN approach to learning. Some visitors behaved as they would in a conventional classroom; they pointed children towards 'right' answers, or marked children's work with ticks and crosses. However, these were a minority; most visitors were enthusiastic and appreciative. They joined sensitively in the children's work, and their enthusiasm sustained the teachers.

One group of teachers wrote a document of advice for visitors, to suggest ways in which visitors could join helpfully in classroom activities. In addition, visitors were given an outline of the group's philosophy and approach to learning. The document included these guidelines:

■ Don't be surprised if what you see is not very different from usual good classroom practice.

■ Calculators will be readily available but children may not choose to use them for the activity at hand. Children may do all their calculating mentally.

■ Our CAN approach aims to develop children's mathematical thinking. This involves such things as encouraging children to question, to choose their own method of recording, to take a 'trial-and-improvement' approach to finding solutions, to work cooperatively and to discuss what they are doing. Visitors are asked not to lead children to 'correct answers'.

■ Visitors are asked not to talk with class teachers while they are teaching. Time will be made available at the end of the session for this.

Certainly, visiting the classrooms gave educators who were not involved in CAN a real-life conception of the project's style of working. It was not possible to gain this impression in the same way by reading the literature or by attending lectures and demonstrations, since much of the project's innovation was based on the style of classroom working which the teachers had developed. However, a balance had to be struck between demonstrating and communicating the project's ways of working and permitting too much visiting to become a damaging interruption to the children's work.

EVALUATION OF THE PROJECT 8

The style of evaluation

At the beginning of the project, the PrIME team consulted educational researchers about the evaluation of CAN. The team was told that it would be difficult to make valid numerical comparisons between project children and control groups of children in other schools. Misleading impressions might be gained from measurements of the comparative performance of children who worked in CAN against other children, as the two groups would have other differences in addition to the fact that they were following different curricula. For example, the project teachers would be supported by team members and advisory teachers; they would also meet regularly and work together in ways in which teachers in control schools might not. Thus, it would not be possible to equate the conditions in project schools and control schools, and this type of quantitative evaluation might be misleading. Consequently, it was decided that the evaluation of the project should be *qualitative*. The evaluator would be asked to observe and report on the activities of teachers and children, and try to evaluate the quality of the observed changes. However, the evaluator would not give mathematical tests to groups of children.

Two evaluators were appointed, both on a part-time basis. Both were very experienced mathematics educators; they had a wide background in primary work, and much experience of working with teachers in INSET. One evaluator concentrated on the work of CAN in England, while the other, a native Welsh speaker, evaluated the work in Dyfed. Both evaluators visited classrooms regularly and talked with children, teachers and headteachers. They also attended teachers' meetings and meetings for parents, and discussed the project with LEA coordinators and mathematics advisers. They attended national project conferences, and met at intervals with the project central team to discuss developments with them.

Each evaluator submitted an annual written report to the project. These reports have been much used in writing this book. The reports show a remarkable similarity in the development of CAN in different parts of the country, as observed by two very different people, and irrespective of whether the schools were working in English or Welsh. The same themes run through all six of the annual reports made by the evaluators; some themes which have not been explicitly discussed in earlier chapters are now described.

From isolation to mutual support

At the beginning of the project, some teachers felt very isolated. In the smaller schools, only one teacher was working on CAN, and there was nobody else in the school with whom that teacher could compare experiences every day. Even in large schools, only a small group of teachers were involved in the project in the first year. The support that the teachers needed had to come from the headteacher and colleagues, from visits from the advisory teacher, and from the teachers' group meetings.

Even joining fully in teachers' groups involved a change of attitude for some teachers. Not all those who joined the project were accustomed to sharing their work and their problems on an equal footing, not only with their own colleagues, but also with teachers from other schools, headteachers, advisory teachers and advisers. Different LEA coordinators also ran their teachers' groups in different ways; some group meetings were more structured than others. Group leaders varied in the amount of direction they gave their teachers; some expected their teachers to take the initiative at once, while others were more directive.

There was some criticism of a lack of detailed direction from the project team. The project team felt that the development of the curriculum should be largely in the hands of the participating teachers; however, not all the teachers at first expected to take this responsibility. For some teachers, responsibility for the mathematics curriculum had previously rested in the hands of a published mathematics scheme; teachers did not always find the transition to taking responsibility themselves an easy one.

However, the wish for direction from elsewhere gradually diminished, and teachers began to value the faith placed in them. At the end of the second year of the project an evaluator wrote:

The perception of teacher autonomy as a desirable component has gradually taken over, and it arose, in almost all cases, from the teacher meetings. In some areas, the teachers have conducted their own meetings, addressing issues seen by them as important, and resulting in the emergence of teacher material associated with the project.

The teachers' groups, by this time, felt ownership of the project. Their children's mathematical development had surprised them, and they were aware of the growth in their own teaching and the change in their attitudes.

And they themselves were the people who had brought about these changes. One headteacher, when talking about CAN to other teachers, would put a blank transparency on the overhead projector and say: 'This was the direction we were given, and after a bit we were glad ... the project was ours.'

Some stages in teacher development

During each year of the project, increasing numbers of teachers became involved. In the first year, all the teachers were new to CAN; in later years, many teachers who had not previously worked in CAN took over project classes. Thus, the project acquired a good deal of experience of the feelings and attitudes of teachers when they first started to work on CAN, and of the ways in which teachers developed their thinking over a period of time. The evaluators were able to describe the stages in professional development through which most teachers passed.

Before they started to work in the project, teachers fell into two groups. Some teachers were apprehensive; others looked forward to CAN with enthusiastic anticipation. Some apprehensive teachers lacked confidence in their ability to innovate; others came from schools where the headteacher or senior members of staff were anxious. Yet others came from schools to which children would transfer; they would be the first teachers in their schools to work in CAN. Enthusiastic teachers had usually had good opportunities to visit project classes and to talk with their teachers, and they were well supported by colleagues.

In either case, most teachers went through an initial period of insecurity and anxiety, when they were bewildered and felt that they were no longer in control of what was happening in the classroom. This stage was followed by a period when teachers became aware that their classroom role must change. During this time, they gradually worked out how to make the changes. However, they continued to feel uncertain, recognising that they had not yet achieved a way of working which would enable the mathematical potential of the children to be fully developed.

Finally, teachers reached a stage in which they accepted their new role, and they were able to plan a classroom environment which allowed children's mathematics to develop freely and appropriately. The teacher had become a stimulator and a facilitator rather than an instructor, and was available at all times to talk with children about the mathematics they were doing. Teachers who have reached this stage show great confidence in the children's capabilities; they know that children are able to become self-critical workers, and that children are able to explain their methods and ways of thinking, and to find their own mistakes. These teachers also recognise that earlier styles of teaching had often, unwittingly, limited children's mathematical development.

One evaluator described the change in teaching in her report on the second year's work:

More teachers have assumed a less interventionist role. They are beginning to see the need to listen to and observe children's behaviour in order to understand the ways in which they learn. Their teaching style is therefore becoming less didactic, more investigative; they are granting to children the same autonomy they are taking on themselves through their involvement in the project.

In many cases, teachers recognised that the changes in their own attitudes and teaching styles would be permanent rather than transitory. One teacher said: 'I don't think any of us would go back to any other way of teaching now that we're into it.' A headteacher gave the opinion that the project would only succeed if teachers were convinced; it is the growth of conviction that enables teachers to change their teaching styles: 'CAN can only be successful if teachers can be convinced.'

The evaluators recognised that, as time went on, the emphasis of the project's work was changing. CAN had begun as a curriculum development project, which intended to devise a suitable number curriculum for a technological age. It was now also developing in other directions. First, it had become a teacher development project, which encouraged teachers to advance their classroom practice. Secondly, the teachers were finding insights into ways in which children learn, and were trying to create classroom conditions which facilitated these ways of learning. These new concerns often became more important in the teachers' thinking than the original curriculum development emphasis. Indeed, some project teachers began to regret the inclusion of the word 'calculator' in the project's name.

Children's attitudes and attainments

The evaluators noticed the children's enthusiastic attitudes to mathematics; their enthusiasm was often much greater than in pre-CAN days. A child remarked about one activity: 'This is brilliant. I could go on doing it all day.' The children's enthusiasm and involvement were confirmed by a teacher: 'I can never get rid of them now. They always used to be up and away at the end of a lesson – now they want to stay on and on.'

Many children continued doing their mathematics at home. One parent mentioned that her older child had never brought mathematics home, while the younger was always drawing attention to mathematical aspects of ordinary life, and thought nothing of doing mathematics at home for fun. Not only had the children become more enthusiastic, but their work also showed much greater mathematical understanding. A parent told an evaluator: 'This CAN thing – I do hope you're going to continue it because my child never made any sense of maths until CAN came along.'

The evaluators noted the children's flexibility, their ease with large numbers, and their ability to recognise number patterns and to be aware of their significance. The children were willing to 'have a go' at any problem, and to persist with it far beyond the teacher's normal expectations of such children.

The children developed a wide variety of methods of non-calculator calculation, but the evaluators noted that some common methods emerged in different parts of the country. These methods often made an intuitive use of basic mathematical principles. For example, children's subtraction methods included some which made use of negative numbers, some which used counting on from the smaller number to the larger, and some which used rounding to the nearest ten followed by a correction. When adding, a majority of children preferred to start with the left-hand digit, and some children did the same in subtraction.

The project classes contained the usual full range of ability found in primary classes. The evaluators reported that the project appeared to confirm the existence of a 'seven year difference' in children's mathematical attainment; this was identified by the Cockcroft Committee (DES 1982). In fact, calculator use seemed to increase the range of attainment; some children seemed to have experienced a great surge forward in achievement, and were working at a much higher level than would previously have been expected of their age group. Other children, who had always found mathematics very difficult, had not surged forward, but were slowly acquiring a feeling for number, and were working with two or three-digit numbers when they might previously have only been expected to use one-digit numbers. The attitudes of these low attainers were also much better than had been expected.

A small minority of children did not take easily to calculator use. Some may have acquired negative attitudes from parents who were opposed to calculator use at school. Other children lacked manual dexterity, a problem which is often associated with learning difficulties. These children needed many opportunities to use the calculator alongside other apparatus; they also needed activities designed to improve their manual dexterity.

Ways of using the calculator

At the beginning of the project, the evaluators reported that calculators were being used in two different ways. First, children used calculators to check their mental calculations; secondly, they used calculators for calculations which they needed to do, but which were too complex to do in their heads.

Gradually, teachers recognised that the calculator had a third use. It was a resource for generating mathematics; it could be used to introduce and develop mathematical ideas and processes. Children were themselves the first to discover this third way of using the calculator. For example, they wanted to use the whole of the eight-digit display; to make sense of what they saw, they needed to find out about large numbers. They used the division key; to make sense of the results, they needed to find out about decimal numbers. They did some subtractions 'the wrong way round' and found that the results were negative numbers. They needed to extend their understanding of the number system to include these numbers. The teachers were quick to realise the possibilities of this way of using the calculator. They began to devise activities and starting points which ensured that children would find and explore new mathematical ideas to help them to make sense of what the calculator showed. Examples of this way of using the calculator are given in Chapter 3, especially in the sections on negative numbers (page 16) and decimals (page 18). These topics, which have not traditionally been included in the curriculum for young children, are made both necessary and accessible by the calculator.

A fourth way of using the calculator is to explore the calculator's keys and operations. For example, the square-root key opened up a whole field of mathematics to the project children; this mathematics included the study of square numbers and the areas of squares and rectangles.

By the end of three years of CAN, some schools were starting to make more complex calculators available to older children, or were inviting children to bring calculators from home. Several new mathematical topics could be investigated when the results of the same calculation on different calculators were compared. These topics include the conventional order in which mathematical operations are carried out, and the notation and meaning of brackets. Teachers may recall these topics from a traditional secondary school curriculum, where the conventions went under the name of BODMAS; the conventions of BODMAS are essential for an understanding of the notation of algebra. Rounding errors in calculation can also be examined by comparing different calculators, as can the very important 'scientific notation' which is used in modern science for enormous and tiny numbers; for example, $1\,234\,000\,000\,000$ can be expressed as 1.234×10^{12}, which can be represented on a calculator display. A few models of calculator also have keys which allow operations on fractions to be explored in an investigational manner, rather than by the traditional didactic teaching of rules such as 'turn it upside down and multiply'.

For most children in the project, the exploration of these topics still lies in the future, but they indicate the wide range of mathematics which calculator use can make accessible and interesting to some upper primary and lower secondary children.

The role of talk

As teachers' styles of teaching changed, and as the work became more investigational, the teachers began to notice the importance of children's talk in CAN.

Through talking, the children were both developing their own thinking and sharing it with each other. In talking with each other and with the teacher, the children extended and elaborated their ideas, and became better communicators of mathematics. One evaluator wrote: 'Talk is emerging as a crucial feature in almost all classrooms.'

Teachers began to realise that the children's talk served other purposes in addition to the sharing and communication of mathematics. Talk could often also serve as a record of the work which a child had accomplished, and it was a very helpful part of the teacher's assessment of children's knowledge and understanding.

In some schools, because of administrative pressures, class sizes increased during the period of the project. Teachers expressed anxiety that, in large classes, the teacher would have less time to join in mathematical talk with each group of children; this would be a serious disadvantage, and might even prevent the project from proceeding as expected. Teachers felt the need to develop their methods of classroom organisation to ensure that time for talking mathematics was still available as the classes grew in size.

In Dyfed, some Welsh-medium schools took part in CAN. This drew attention to other aspects of the interplay between language and mathematics. Not all the children in the Welsh-medium schools were first-language Welsh speakers. The Welsh evaluator reported that the language which was spoken in the classroom had no effect on the suitability of CAN for the children. She wrote:

❝ CAN activities have proceeded as they would have done in English. There are, however, positive effects on the development of the Welsh language. Children have required additional vocabulary and there has been greater emphasis on discussion. ❞

Another Welsh-speaking evaluator worked on other aspects of PrIME's work in Wales. On one occasion, he also visited the CAN schools, where he noticed the same feature:

❝ CAN is a catalyst for talking, discussing and reasoning, and has proved very beneficial as a means of strengthening both languages in a truly bilingual context. ❞

The member of the project team who worked with the Welsh schools was English, but was learning Welsh. She noticed that different languages produce different learning problems in mathematics. English-speaking children often find the 'teen' numbers from 13 to 19 confusing because, for example, in the word 'thirteen' the 'three' is said before the 'ten', whereas in 'twenty-three' and 'thirty-three', the 'tens' are said first. This irregularity does not occur in Welsh. The Welsh words involved are 'un' (one), 'dau' (two), 'tri' (three) 'deg' (ten); thirteen is 'un deg tri', twenty-three is 'dau ddeg tri', thirty-three is 'tri deg tri'. Welsh-speaking children are not observed to have the same problems as English-speaking children in learning about the 'teen' numbers.

In England, the project was not based in schools with large numbers of ethnic minority children, so an evaluation could not be made of the effect of CAN on children for whom English was not their first language. However, the Welsh experience suggests that the importance of talk in CAN might strengthen the learning of English by linguistic minority children, as well as strengthening all children's understanding of mathematics. Mother-tongue helpers might also be able to help some children to use the structures of their first language to grasp some features of the structure of number.

Assessment and record-keeping

The recording of children's attainment is a comparatively easy task for teachers if a published mathematics scheme is in use, and if each child proceeds page by page through it. All that is needed is for the teacher to record the number of the page or the workcard on which each child is working. However, in these rigidly structured schemes, a child's understanding does not always keep in step with the order of the pages. Sometimes a child's understanding may lag behind the page, even if the child has successfully completed the page; sometimes understanding may be in advance of that needed for the page. Whether this style of mathematics teaching is used, or if a more flexible style is adopted, it is always the case that the assessment of a child's mathematical understanding is much more complex than merely recording the work that the child does. Understanding of mathematics is a many-dimensional web, full of links which an individual child has made, and other links which have still not been made.

When the teachers who worked in CAN began to move away from using published mathematics schemes, the importance and the difficulty of assessment and record-keeping loomed much larger in their thinking, and in their conversations with the evaluators. Many teachers began to do a good deal of informal assessment of children's understanding by observing them at work, and by talking with them, as well as by reading their written work. It was, however, difficult to devise methods of keeping good records of the growth of the complex web of children's understanding. Indeed, some teachers were thinking about this problem for the first time, as their realisation grew that mathematics learning is not a linear progression along which all children proceed in the same order.

Different groups of teachers tackled the problem of recording children's progress in different ways; at one national project conference, the groups pooled, discussed and developed their ideas. Some groups tried to note down the 'highlights' achieved by each child. One group worked to produce a diagrammatic progress chart which could be filled in for each child. One teacher built up a record book in which, for each child, dated pieces of work were filed to serve as a record of progress. By the end of three years of the project, further experiment with methods of recording children's progress was still needed.

After three years, this aspect of the project was overtaken by the need for schools to devise methods of recording children's progress in the National Curriculum. It may be that the lists of Statements of Attainment in the National Curriculum in mathematics will provide teachers with a structure which makes it easier to record children's progress in CAN. At the time of writing, it is much too early to predict outcomes from the careful records of children's progress in all aspects of mathematics, which are required by the National Curriculum in mathematics. Even if record-keeping becomes easier, the problem of assessing the levels of children's mathematical understanding will remain a complex one.

A quantitative evaluation

Although the style of most of the project's evaluation was qualitative, circumstances in one LEA forced some *quantitative* evaluation on the project, in the years before the National Curriculum in mathematics and its testing were introduced. The Suffolk LEA had for some years tested all children in mathematics during the school years in which they attained the ages of nine, 11 and 13. Thus, comparisons could be made between the mathematical performance on the Suffolk 8+ Test of the Suffolk children who were working in CAN and other Suffolk children. The Suffolk LEA appointed an advisory teacher who was not involved in CAN to carry out comparisons between the attainment of project children and others (Oram 1989).

Before this evaluation was carried out, the 8+ Test was revised by Suffolk teachers so that it would not give undue advantage either to children who habitually did, or did not, use calculators. The 8+ Test became a test of children's understanding, not only of number, but of a variety of mathematical ideas. However, all children were required to use a calculator for a few items: the encouragement of calculator use had been the LEA's policy for several years. The test and its results were analysed by the National Foundation for Educational Research. Usually, 90% of Suffolk children took a written test, while the other 10% took a practical test.

The first occasion on which project children took the Suffolk 8+ Test was in February 1989, when they had worked in CAN for a period of either four terms or seven terms. None of the project schools fell into the sample which carried out the practical test, so all comparisons were made on the written test. A total of 116 project children were tested, and their performance was compared with that of 116 other children chosen at random from the non-project children in Suffolk. The numbers are small, so any conclusions drawn from the results must be viewed with caution.

For each of the 36 items of the test, scores were given in terms of the percentage of pupils who gave satisfactory answers to that item. Figure 8.1 shows the results for the first and last items of the test. To counter the difficulties which some children might have in reading the test, the class teacher was asked to read each of the first 18 test items to the children; they then proceeded with the remainder of the test at their own pace, reading the items themselves.

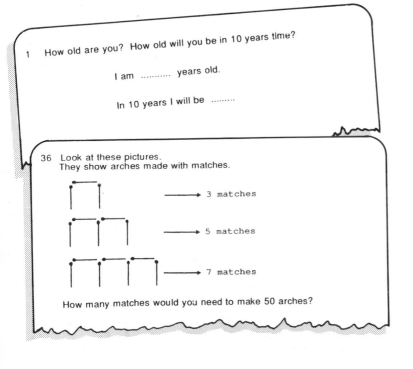

	CAN	non-CAN
% of valid responses	96.5	94.8
% not attempting item	0.0	0.0
% of valid responses	8.6	4.3
% not attempting item	14.7	16.4

Figure 8.1

In 28 of the 36 test items, a higher percentage of project children than other children gave correct responses. In 11 of these items, the success rate of the project children was 10% or more higher than that of the other children, and in one item, it was as much as 30% higher. In the remaining eight items, the non-project children performed as well or better than the project children. However, the maximum percentage by which the other children exceeded the project children was 5.3%. Figure 8.2 shows the 11 questions on which the proportion of successful project children was 10% or more greater than that of other children. They are ranked in order of the difference between project and non-project children. Figure 8.3 (using the same ranking) shows the eight questions on which other children were at least as successful as the project children.

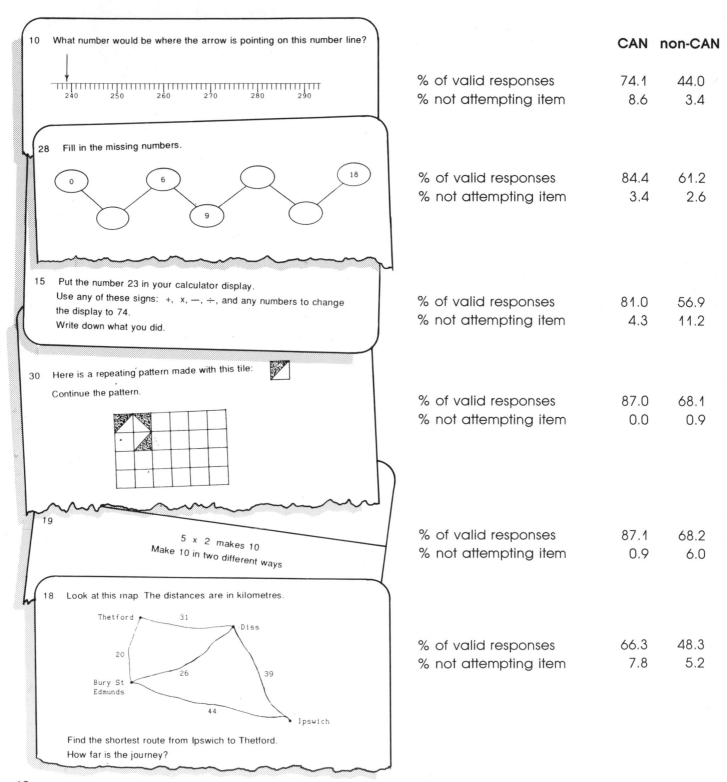

	CAN	non-CAN
10 What number would be where the arrow is pointing on this number line?		
% of valid responses	74.1	44.0
% not attempting item	8.6	3.4
28 Fill in the missing numbers.		
% of valid responses	84.4	61.2
% not attempting item	3.4	2.6
15 Put the number 23 in your calculator display. Use any of these signs: +, x, —, ÷, and any numbers to change the display to 74. Write down what you did.		
% of valid responses	81.0	56.9
% not attempting item	4.3	11.2
30 Here is a repeating pattern made with this tile: Continue the pattern.		
% of valid responses	87.0	68.1
% not attempting item	0.0	0.9
19 5 x 2 makes 10. Make 10 in two different ways		
% of valid responses	87.1	68.2
% not attempting item	0.9	6.0
18 Look at this map The distances are in kilometres. Find the shortest route from Ipswich to Thetford. How far is the journey?		
% of valid responses	66.3	48.3
% not attempting item	7.8	5.2

In 20 items, a higher percentage of non-project children did not attempt the item. Fourteen of these items were in the later part of the test, where there was no teacher support in reading. This might suggest that project children are more able to work by themselves, without the support of the teacher.

The results of this test are very encouraging, and suggest that, at the age of eight, children who work in CAN are able to do better than other children on a general test of mathematics. However, there remain some reservations about the comparability of project classes with other classes (see page 55), and the samples of children tested were not large. The project would be rightly criticised if it made too large a claim on the basis of this one test.

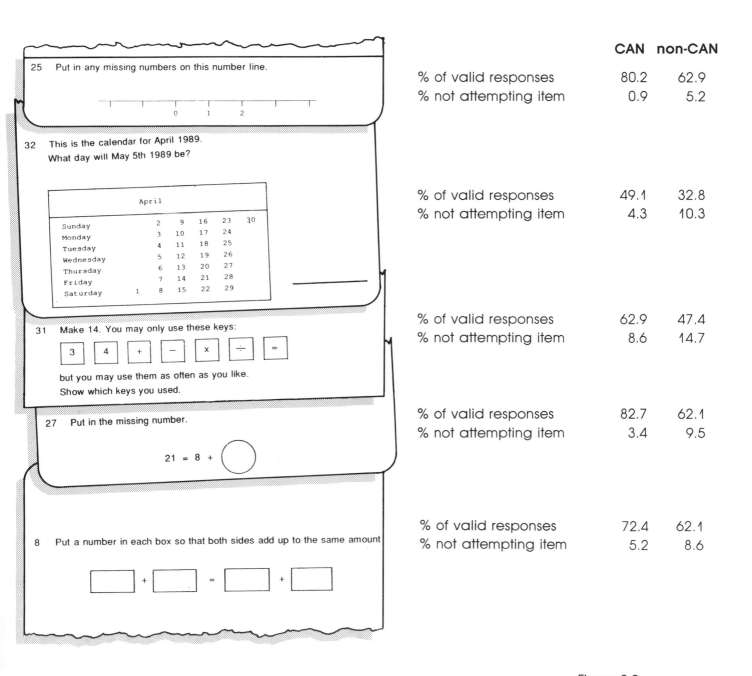

	CAN	non-CAN
% of valid responses	80.2	62.9
% not attempting item	0.9	5.2
% of valid responses	49.1	32.8
% not attempting item	4.3	10.3
% of valid responses	62.9	47.4
% not attempting item	8.6	14.7
% of valid responses	82.7	62.1
% not attempting item	3.4	9.5
% of valid responses	72.4	62.1
% not attempting item	5.2	8.6

Figure 8.2

The Suffolk 8+ Test evaluates only one aspect of mathematics teaching and learning – the children's ability to complete a short-answer pencil-and-paper test. The qualitative evaluation, on the other hand, has shown the effects of CAN on teachers and children in other aspects of mathematics teaching and learning which cannot be tested in the same way. These aspects include the attitudes of children and teachers to mathematics, the children's mathematical thinking in longer mathematical tasks and in cross-curricular tasks, and the styles of teaching and learning which are found in the classroom. Here, too, the results are very positive.

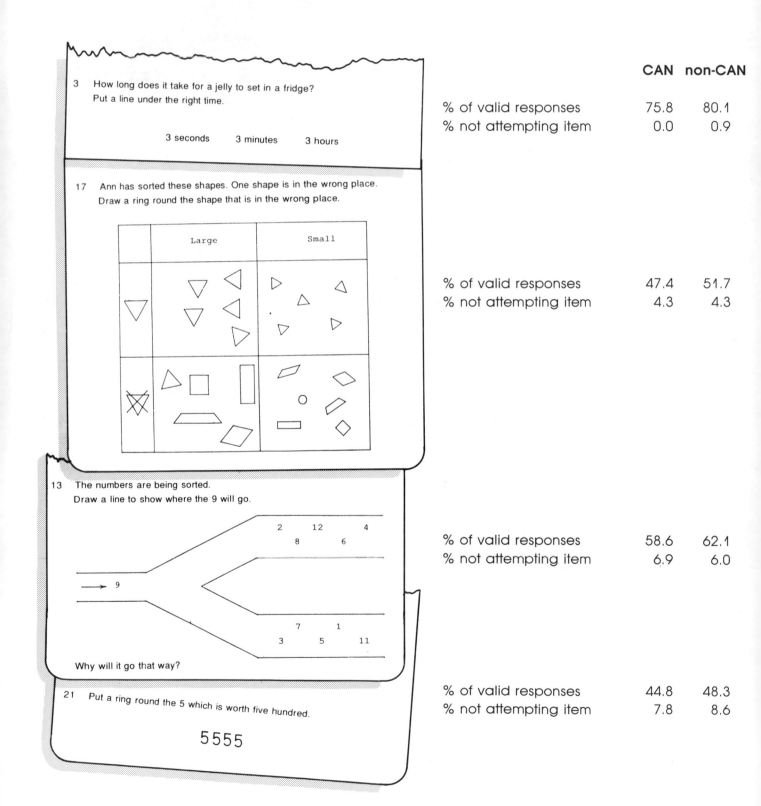

	CAN	non-CAN
3 How long does it take for a jelly to set in a fridge? Put a line under the right time. 3 seconds 3 minutes 3 hours		
% of valid responses	75.8	80.1
% not attempting item	0.0	0.9
17 Ann has sorted these shapes. One shape is in the wrong place. Draw a ring round the shape that is in the wrong place.		
% of valid responses	47.4	51.7
% not attempting item	4.3	4.3
13 The numbers are being sorted. Draw a line to show where the 9 will go. Why will it go that way?		
% of valid responses	58.6	62.1
% not attempting item	6.9	6.0
21 Put a ring round the 5 which is worth five hundred. 5555		
% of valid responses	44.8	48.3
% not attempting item	7.8	8.6

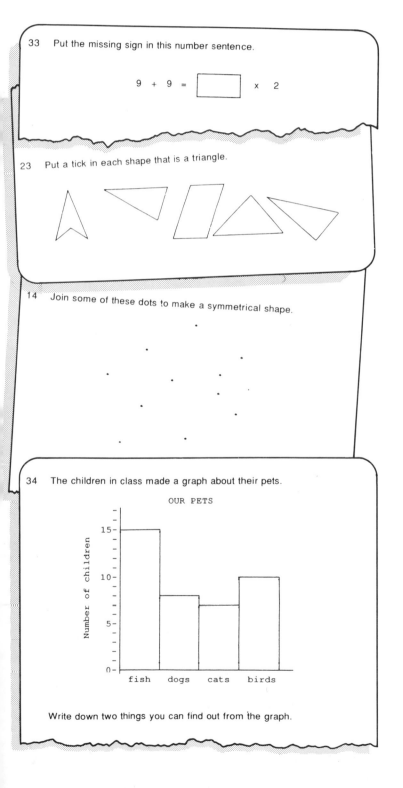

	CAN	non-CAN
33 Put the missing sign in this number sentence.		
% of valid responses	10.3	12.9
% not attempting item	6.9	5.2

33 Put the missing sign in this number sentence.

$$9 + 9 = \boxed{} \times 2$$

23 Put a tick in each shape that is a triangle.

	CAN	non-CAN
% of valid responses	67.2	69.0
% not attempting item	0.0	3.4

14 Join some of these dots to make a symmetrical shape.

	CAN	non-CAN
% of valid responses	56.0	56.9
% not attempting item	4.3	3.4

34 The children in class made a graph about their pets.

OUR PETS

Write down two things you can find out from the graph.

	CAN	non-CAN
% of valid responses	57.8	57.8
% not attempting item	14.7	16.4

Figure 8.3

9 THE NATIONAL CURRICULUM AND CAN

Introduction of the National Curriculum

Readers outside the United Kingdom may not be aware that a National Curriculum in mathematics was introduced in 1989 for all state schools in England and Wales. Primary schools must ensure that all their pupils follow this curriculum in the 'core' subjects of mathematics, science and English, and in six other 'foundation' subjects. The curriculum in each subject is described by means of a number of *Attainment Targets* at ten *Levels of Attainment*. At the time of going to press, there are 14 Attainment Targets in mathematics (but see notice on page 4). At each Level, each Attainment Target consists of several *Statements of Attainment*. Children will be tested at the ages of seven, 11, 14 and 16, and will also be assessed by their teachers on each Attainment Target. As a result of these tests and assessments, each child will be assigned a level between one and ten for each Attainment Target.

Thus, it is expected that each primary class will contain children who are working at different Levels from some of their peers, and at different Levels on different Attainment Targets. The table below outlines the Levels at which it is planned that primary children will be working in mathematics, on average, across the Attainment Targets. It is expected that a child of average attainment will progress at the rate of about one Level every two years, although some will progress faster than this, and some more slowly. The Attainment Targets are intended to constitute an assessment syllabus; they do not attempt to list the full detail needed in a teaching syllabus. Moreover, neither the styles of teaching to be used nor the resources are prescribed.

Levels of the National Curriculum in mathematics in the primary years

Level	Age
1	Least able 7-year-olds
2	The majority of 7-year-olds
3	Most able 7-year-olds 9-year-olds of average attainment
4	11-year-olds of average attainment
6	Most able 11-year-olds

The National Curriculum may have a considerable effect on CAN, as it is no longer possible for state schools to determine their own curriculum in mathematics. In order to discuss any changes in CAN which may be needed, the likenesses and differences between CAN and National Curriculum mathematics will now be described.

A broad curriculum

The National Curriculum in mathematics is a broad curriculum, which ensures that children follow a balanced range of mathematical topics from the earliest levels. The Attainment Targets cover the topics of *number, algebra, measures, shape and space, handling data* and *using and applying mathematics.* Each of these topics features in the curriculum from Level 1. Perhaps the most surprising topic to occur as early as Level 1 is algebra. However, the approach used is to build up algebraic ideas gradually from number patterns, from function machines and in other ways that are appropriate for young children. These ideas lead naturally to algebraic generalisations and notation at higher levels.

The other topic whose occurrence has surprised some primary teachers is handling data. This topic covers the collection, recording and handling of data gathered from simple surveys. The representation of data in graphs, charts and tables is also studied, as are basic ideas of probability which lead at later levels to an understanding of statistics. The modern world makes increasing use of statistical data; the topic of handling data forms an appropriate introduction to this feature of the mathematics of everyday life.

The other topics included in National Curriculum mathematics (number, measures, shape and space and using and applying mathematics) have formed part of the primary mathematics curriculum for many years, but number has not always been appropriately balanced against other topics. In some classrooms, too, children have had few opportunities to use and apply the mathematics they are learning to a wide range of problems.

The National Curriculum is laid down in terms of 'subjects' such as mathematics and English. However, teachers have also been supplied with *Mathematics: Non-Statutory Guidance* (NCC 1989), which gives advice on implementing the mathematics curriculum. This guidance urges the importance of cross-curricular work, and urges primary schools to give thought to:

Identifying the opportunities that exist for developing mathematics out of cross-curricular topic work, through, for instance, the pupils' own interests and experiences or the environment and life of the school.

[Section F, para 2.2]

The CAN project was originally intended to develop only the number aspect of mathematics. The project has always urged teachers to continue to work on other aspects of mathematics alongside CAN. As teachers have developed their teaching styles in CAN, and as the work has become more investigational, it has become very clear how important is a broad curriculum in mathematics, and how vital it is for children to be able to use and apply their mathematics to a range of problems and investigations. Cross-curricular work which includes mathematics has also become an increasing feature of the work in many classrooms in project schools. These aspects of National Curriculum mathematics will be welcomed by most teachers who work with project classes; they will ensure that the excitement of exploring numbers which CAN has engendered is balanced by excitement at exploring other mathematical topics, and of finding mathematics in the range of cross-curricular topics which are studied in primary classrooms.

Using and applying mathematics

The National Curriculum in mathematics explicitly emphasises the importance of **using and applying mathematics.** Two of the Attainment Targets are concerned not with the content of mathematics, but with the **uses and applications** of mathematics to a variety of situations and problems. In *Mathematics: Non-Statutory Guidance* (NCC 1989), it is pointed out that:

Experience suggests that an approach in which pupils are required to use and apply their developing knowledge and skills leads to more effective learning.

Tackling problems, both of the practical, 'real life' sort, and within mathematics itself, ***motivates and requires*** *the learning of further skills and the development of greater understanding.*

[Section D, para 1.2]

The Attainment Targets on using and applying mathematics contain examples drawn from all areas of mathematical content. Thus, teachers need to give attention to using and applying all mathematical topics. The Non-Statutory Guidance urges that:

As a consequence of the interaction between learning and using mathematics, work related to Attainment Targets 1 and 9 [Using and Applying Mathematics] cannot be tackled in isolation from the rest of the programmes of study. Similarly, work related to Attainment Targets 2-8 and 10-14 [mathematical content] cannot be satisfactorily pursued independently from that related to Attainment Targets 1 and 9. [Section D, para 1.5]

The Non-Statutory Guidance lists a variety of activities which are appropriate to using and applying mathematics. These activities include practical work and the use of physical materials, real-life problems, problems drawn from the whole curriculum, and investigating within mathematics itself. Schools are urged to ensure that using and applying mathematics plays a full part in the curriculum:

The National Curriculum requires all schools to address this issue, and to develop a teaching and learning approach in which the uses and applications of mathematics permeate and influence all work in mathematics. [Section D, para 3.2]

The Attainment Targets on using and applying mathematics are structured under three themes: **using mathematics, communicating in mathematics,** and **developing ideas of argument and proof.** The theme of 'using mathematics' is concerned with the planning which children need to do when starting a task, and the checking needed while carrying it out. Examples of Statements of Attainment are:

Use materials provided for a task. [AT 1, Level 1]

Select the materials and the mathematics to use for a task; check results and consider whether they are sensible.
[AT 1, Level 3]

Select the materials and the mathematics to use for a task; check there is sufficient information; work methodically and review progress. [AT 1, Level 5]

It is clear that a 'task' means more than the usual textbook exercises. At least some tasks need to be substantial pieces of work, involving choice, initiative and planning. The Statements of Attainment concerned with communicating in mathematics bring out similar points:

Explain work being done and record findings systematically. [AT 1, Level 3]

Record findings and present them in oral, written or visual form as appropriate. [AT 1, Level 4]

Hence, by Level 4, children should be accustomed to reporting on their work orally as well as in writing and drawing, and they should expect to share some of their work with the group or the class.

The third theme is concerned with developing ideas of argument and proof. Some Statements of Attainment are:

Make predictions based on experience. [AT 1, Level 1]

Make and test predictions. [AT 1, Level 3]

Use examples to test statements or definitions.
[AT 1, Level 4]

Thus, children need to explain and justify their own mathematical thinking; they will need to gain experience of mathematical thinking by carrying out investigations and tackling problems. Even at Level 1, children are expected to make sensible predictions of what will happen during a task.

In some primary schools, the new emphasis on using and applying mathematics will require changes in the approach to mathematics teaching. However, working on CAN has already encouraged project schools to move in this direction. Investigational and open-ended work have become widespread, and children often carry out substantial tasks. Many examples are given in Chapter 5, pages 35 to 43. Teachers have also developed their skills in listening and responding to children's ideas, and they value the contribution which talk can make to children's learning (see page 58).

Of course, project schools will need to develop their work in response to using and applying mathematics. However, a good foundation for this development is provided by the fact that children are expected to use their own ideas and to solve problems for themselves, with support from the teacher. In some classrooms, it will be necessary to develop real-life problem solving – but that is also the case in many non-project classrooms. In some classrooms, further attention will need to be given to the 'presentation' of mathematical work orally, in writing and in drawing. In general, however, project teachers are able to tackle using and applying mathematics with confidence, because their work has already taken them in this direction.

Understanding number and number operations

Three Attainment Targets (2, 3 and 4) in mathematics are concerned with the topic of number. These Attainment Targets cover, respectively, *understanding number and number notation, understanding number operations and using appropriate methods of calculation,* and *estimation and approximation in number.* A fourth Attainment Target (5) is shared between the topics of number and algebra. It concerns the *recognition and use of patterns, relationships and sequences, and making generalisations.*

The most able 11-year-olds are expected to achieve Level 6 on the mathematics Attainment Targets. Between Levels 1 and 6, Attainment Target 2, Understand Number and Number Notation, deals with whole numbers, negative numbers, decimals, fractions and percentages. Operations on these numbers are dealt with in Attainment Target 3, Understand Number Operations and Make Use of Appropriate Methods of Calculation. The ways in which these topics are developed are not always those which are found in traditional schemes of work.

The route by which whole number ideas are built up in the National Curriculum is one with which all teachers are familiar. However, children are expected to understand all four of the number operations at quite an early stage, and to use calculators when they cannot carry out the calculation without a calculator. Some of the Statements of Attainment are:

Count, read, write and order numbers to at least 10; know that the size of a set is given by the last number in the count. [AT 2, Level 1]

Read, write and order numbers to at least 1000; use the knowledge that the position of a digit indicates its value. [AT 2, Level 3]

Solve problems involving multiplication or division of whole numbers or money, using a calculator where necessary. [AT 3, Level 3]

The introduction of negative numbers at Level 3 came as a surprise to many teachers of young children:

Appreciate the meaning of negative whole numbers in familiar contexts. [AT 2, Level 3]

One of the examples which illustrates this target is 'Understand a negative output on a calculator'. However, no calculations involving negative numbers are required until Level 5, where an example is 'Calculate the increase in temperature from –4°C to +10°C'.

The methods by which decimals are introduced do not apparently take much account of the availability of calculators:

Use decimal notation as the conventional way of recording in money. [AT 2, Level 3]

Use, with understanding, decimal notation to two decimal places in the context of measurement. [AT 2, Level 4]

Read, write and order decimals; appreciate the relationship between place values. [AT 2, Level 6]

However, it is certainly expected that calculators will be used in establishing ideas about decimals; an example at Level 3 is 'Know ... that 3.6 on a calculator means £3.60 in the context of money'. In fact, at Level 3, the Target on multiplication and division, which allows the use of calculators, will ensure that children have some acquaintance with decimals in the context of division. It must be emphasised that the Attainment Targets constitute an assessment syllabus, not a teaching syllabus. It would not be appropriate to make a formal assessment of children's very early ideas about decimals; however, children meet decimals as soon as they start to use the division key of the calculator, and the teaching needs to build on this.

Children are expected to know the meaning of fractions and percentages, but traditional calculations with fractions are not required until Level 8, and so they do not feature in the primary school curriculum.

Understand the meaning of 'a half' and 'a quarter'.
[AT 2, Level 2]

Understand and use equivalence of fractions and of ratios; relate these to decimals and percentages. [AT 2, Level 6]

Calculate with fractions. [AT 3, Level 8]

Chapters 3, 4 and 5 of this book give many examples of the understanding of number and number operations shown by project children aged six to nine. The availability of calculators seems to accelerate children's grasp of large numbers. At the age of six, Gary (see page 12) was able to split up 173 into 100, 70, 3 and 0. Kelly and Janice (see page 15) were able to calculate the cost of a farm visit for 88 children who each paid £2.50. They did this calculation without calculators; children are not expected to multiply a three-digit number by a two-digit number without a calculator until Level 5.

The calculator gives children an early familiarity with negative numbers; many teachers reinforce this by using number-lines showing positive and negative numbers. One child (see page 18) worked out that $(+1) - (-1)$ is 2 because the difference between +1 and −1 is 2. It seems likely that the same child would be able to work out the rise in temperature from −4°C to +10°C; this calculation is given as an example at Level 5.

The position about project chidren's understanding of decimals and fractions is more complex. Many children know the decimal equivalents of simple fractions, and Michael and Richard (see page 22) were able to give some explanation of the reason that 0.25 is the decimal equivalent of one quarter. However, it seems unlikely that any children who have worked on CAN have a full understanding of decimal place value before the age of nine.

Similar remarks apply to the understanding of percentages. No work on percentages has been observed in CAN in the six-to-nine age-group. However, some ten and eleven-year-old project children were seen carrying out an activity in which they had to order a set of number cards, each of which was written in one of four notations. For example, the cards might show $^{40}/_{100}$, 0.7, $^{6}/_{10}$ and 80%; the children found it very easy to order the cards in descending order.

In general, it seems that project children will have few problems in meeting the Attainment Targets which require understanding of number concepts and operations. In many cases, the children's understanding is likely to be in advance of that traditionally expected of children of their age and ability. However, this must remain a matter for speculation for some time to come; the first group of children to be assessed on the National Curriculum at the age of 11 will not be assessed until 1994.

Methods of calculation

The National Curriculum requires children to use three methods of calculation, in appropriate circumstances:

■ Mental methods.

■ Pencil-and-paper methods.

■ Using a calculator.

The Attainment Targets show which methods are regarded as appropriate for particular types of calculation.

Some examples of *mental* calculation are given in the following Statements of Attainment:

(Using whole numbers) add or subtract mentally two 2-digit numbers; add mentally several single-digit numbers.
[AT 3, Level 4]

Multiply and divide mentally single-digit multiples of powers of 10 with whole number answers.
[AT 3, Level 5]

The example which illustrates the Level 5 statement is:

Calculate 70×100 leading to $70 \times 500 = 35000$; $8000 \div 10$ leading to $800 \div 20 = 40$.

Chapter 4 provides many examples of project children between the ages of six and nine performing mental addition and subtraction of two-digit numbers. This type of calculation is not expected to give the children any difficulty at Level 4.

However, it is not easy to find examples of children using the Statement of Attainment on multiples of powers of ten. The examples given are of intermediate steps in mental calculations, and the only way to find out whether a child has actually used this method is to talk with the child. However, some children's methods of non-calculator multiplication probably incorporate these processes. For example, Hannah (see page 28) started to multiply 54 by 62 by multiplying 50 by 60; the result was probably based on her knowledge of five times six.

Some Statements of Attainment either require the use of a calculator, or allow it to be used if necessary. Examples are:

Read a calculator display to the nearest whole number.
[AT 4, Level 4]

Know how to interpret results on a calculator which have rounding errors.

Example
Interpret $7 \div 3 \times 3 = 6.9999999$ if it occurs on a calculator.
[AT 4, Level 4]

Calculate fractions and percentages of quantities using a calculator where necessary. [AT 3, Level 5]

These Statements of Attainment seem appropriate for children who are experienced calculator users. Moreover, not only the children who are involved in CAN, but all children, will now be required to use calculators from Level 3, and so will become experienced calculator users.

Some Statements of Attainment require children to use **non-calculator** methods of calculation:

Without a calculator add or subtract two 3-digit numbers, multiply a 2-digit number by a single-digit number and divide a 2-digit number by a single-digit number.
[AT 3, Level 4]

(Using whole numbers) understand and use non-calculator methods by which a 3-digit number is multiplied by a 2-digit number and a 3-digit number is divided by a 2-digit number. [AT 3, Level 5]

The National Curriculum in mathematics never requires the use of particular non-calculator methods of calculation; it only requires that a calculator should not be used. The traditional vertical pencil-and-paper methods are acceptable, as are the children's own methods.

These targets seem suitable for project children who are accustomed to devising their own methods of calculation. Several methods which children have devised for non-calculator addition and subtraction are described on pages 26 and 27. By the age of nine, some project children were also beginning to develop their own non-calculator methods for multiplication and division (see pages 27 to 33). This development has continued as the children have grown older, and Figures 9.1 and 9.2 give examples provided by children aged nine and ten. Figure 9.1 shows the methods that two children in the same class used to multiply 146 by 24. In both cases the answer is written at the top, with detail of the steps of the calculation underneath. In Figure 9.2, a Welsh-speaking child is finding how many cupfuls, of volume 160 millilitres, can be obtained from containers of various sizes, and how much is left over.

$$146 \times 24 = 3504$$
$$146 \times 2 = 292$$
$$292 \times 10 = 2920$$
$$292 \times 2 = 584$$
$$2920 + 584 = 3504$$

$$146 \times 24 = 3504$$
$$100 \times 24 = 2400$$
$$46 \times 24 = 1104 \qquad 46 \times 10 = 460$$
$$46 \times 10 = 460$$
$$460 \times 2 = 920$$
$$46 \times 2 = 92$$
$$92 \times 2 = 184$$
$$920 + 184 = 1104$$

Figure 9.1

$$2200 \div 160$$
$$160 \times 10 = 1600$$
$$160 \times 13 = 2080$$
$$160 \times 14 = 2240$$

13 cwpan   20ml ar ôl

$$2140 \div 160$$
$$160 \times 10 = 1600$$
$$160 \times 11 = 1760$$
$$160 \times 13 = 2080$$
$$160 \times 14 = 2240$$

13 cwpan   60ml ar ôl

Figure 9.2

The NCC's Non-Statutory Guidance on calculation

Teachers have been provided with *Mathematics: Non-Statutory Guidance* (NCC 1989), to help them to implement National Curriculum mathematics in their classrooms. The document also deals with points that cannot be explained in the Attainment Targets. Section E of the Non-Statutory Guidance is entitled 'Pupils doing calculations'; it advises teachers on the three methods of calculation.

This advice is very supportive of a CAN approach to calculation. For example, it is suggested that:

> *In order to progress through the levels, pupils, at every stage, should be encouraged to develop **their own** methods for doing calculations. As they develop in confidence and understanding, pupils will refine and develop their methods, building up a range of ways of tackling calculations.* [Section E, para 1.4]

Pencil-and-paper methods are regarded as important methods of calculation, but the Non-Statutory Guidance does not take the traditional view of what is meant by pencil-and-paper methods. Both in everyday discussion and in the literature, 'pencil-and-paper methods' often mean the traditional vertical methods of carrying out addition, subtraction, multiplication and division. In reality, however, pencil and paper are writing implements. When they are used in calculation, pencil and paper enable intermediate results to be written down if the calculation is too complex to be carried out entirely mentally. In any pencil-and-paper method of calculation, a complex calculation is broken down into small parts which can be carried out mentally, and the partial results are recorded and combined together. This can be done in very many ways. The document points out that:

> *The term 'pencil and paper methods' encompasses a wide range of formal and informal techniques and methods.*
> [Section E, para 3.1]

Two examples are given in the Non-Statutory Guidance of pupils' recording of non-traditional pencil-and-paper methods: addition (Figure 9.3a) and multiplication (Figure 9.3b). The multiplication calculation is prefaced by a problem:

> *The Headmaster has asked all the pupils in the school to each bring 24 comics for the comic stall at the school fete. If there are 357 pupils in the school, how many comics should be brought for the stall?* [Section E, para 3.2]

Figure 9.3c from the document shows the traditional vertical method of carrying out the same calculation.

The first two examples might well have come from the CAN project. They show clearly the individual methods that children of different ages and attainments use when they record their calculations.

The Non-Statutory Guidance also discusses the damage that can be done to children's mathematical thinking by excessive practice of traditional calculations out of context:

> *Excessive practice of traditional pencil and paper methods out of context will act in an inhibiting way to the overall aim of raising standards in mathematics. The attainment targets in mathematics do not specify approaches to be adopted in developing pencil and paper methods, but encourage an approach which is built on increasing fluency with, and understanding of, number and number operations.* [Section E, para 3.3]

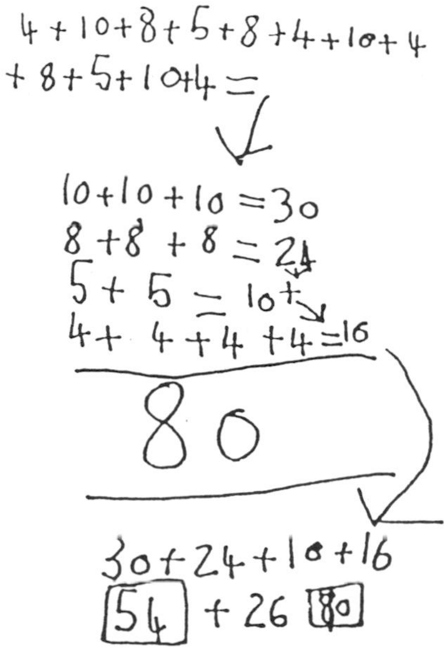

Figure 9.3a

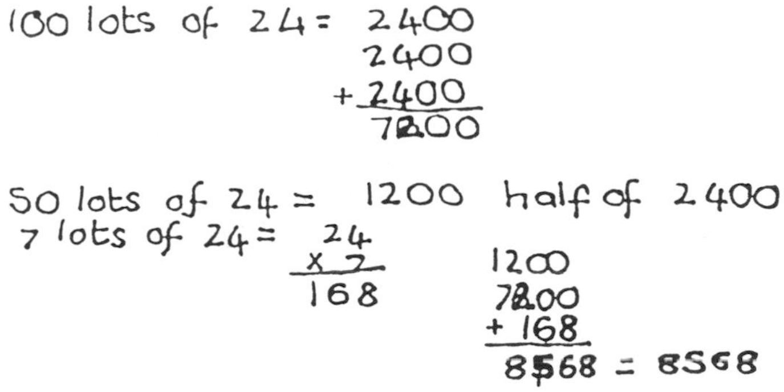

Figure 9.3b

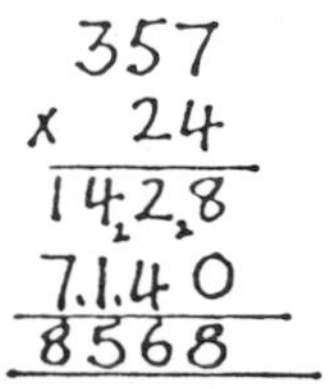

Figure 9.3c

The importance of mental calculation is also emphasised in the Non-Statutory Guidance, which quotes from the Cockcroft Report (DES 1982):

We believe that the decline of mental and oral work within mathematics classrooms represents a failure to recognise the central place which 'working in the head' occupies throughout mathematics. [Para 255]

Teachers are urged to develop pupils' mental calculation through such methods as exploring numbers, encouraging familiarity with addition and multiplication facts, and asking children to compare strategies for their more complex mental calculations. The Non-Statutory Guidance stresses that:

This central place of mental methods should be reflected in an approach that encourages pupils to look on these methods as a 'first resort' when a calculation is needed. [Section E, para 2.2]

Many children who work in CAN make much use of mental methods of calculation. This has helped their teachers to appreciate the central importance of mental calculation (see Chapter 4, pages 24 to 34).

The Non-Statutory Guidance calls attention to the value of calculators, not only for calculation, but also for developing children's understanding of number:

The attainment targets ... demonstrate a recognition that calculators provide a powerful and versatile tool for pupils to use in both the development of their understanding of number and for doing calculations. Calculators are now an established item of classroom equipment, and should be available for pupils to use at all four key stages. [Section E, para 4.1]

All calculator users occasionally make mistakes through pressing the wrong keys. The Non-Statutory Guidance points out that pupils need mental methods to estimate the expected result of a calculation, and to check that the calculator's result is reasonable. Teachers are also urged to give pupils opportunities to use calculators as a powerful means of exploring numbers, which gives insight into number and number relationships. Many examples of children's explorations of number are given in Chapters 3, 4 and 5. The Non-Statutory Guidance concludes its comments on methods of calculation as follows:

For most practical purposes, pupils will use mental methods or a calculator to tackle problems involving calculations. Thus the heavy emphasis placed on teaching standard written methods for calculations in the past needs to be re-examined. [Section E, para 5.3]

In general, the Non-Statutory Guidance is well in accord with the Cockcroft Report's guidance, which included such points as:

We believe that it is not profitable for pupils to spend time practising the traditional method of setting out long division on paper, but that they should normally use a calculator. [Para 390]

We wish to stress that the availability of a calculator in no way reduces the need for mathematical understanding on the part of the person who is using it. [Para 378]

Other aspects of number

The two remaining Attainment Targets on number are concerned with *estimation and approximation in number* and the *recognition and use of patterns, relationships and sequences, and making generalisations.* The latter target is attributed to both the topics of number and algebra.

Some Statements of Attainment concerned with estimation are:

Make use of estimation and approximation to check the validity of addition and subtraction calculations. [AT 4, Level 4]

Make use of estimation and approximation to check that the results of multiplication and division problems involving whole numbers are of the right order. [AT 4, Level 6]

While these are very important skills for children to acquire, it is difficult to check that children have actually used them on a particular occasion. Children can be asked to record an estimate, as was Carla (see pages 33 and 34), but it is difficult to be certain that she made her estimate by rounding the numbers to the nearest ten and subtracting, before she carried out the full calculation. As a competent mental calculator, she might have done the complete subtraction mentally, and rounded the answer to obtain an 'estimate'. Similarly, when a child uses a calculator, the only evidence that a mental estimate was made may be that the calculation was repeated on the calculator. Again, it is difficult to tell whether the child made an estimate which did not agree with the calculator's result, or whether the calculation was merely repeated as an easy way of verifying its correctness.

Some of the other Statements of Attainment concerned with estimation are easier to assess:

Use and refine 'trial and improvement' methods. [AT 4, Level 5]

Approximate using a specified number of significant figures or decimal places. [AT 4, Level 5]

These statements are presumably placed at Level 5 because a certain sophistication is expected in the methods used. However, when Donna, at the age of six, found the amount of milk drunk by the whole school, she approximated the number in each class by rounding to the nearest ten, and obtained an estimated total by adding these, before she carried out the full calculation.

Similarly, children use 'trial and improvement' methods on the calculator from a very early stage. For example, an often-used activity for young children asks them to make a loop of numbers, ending up with the number that they started with (Figure 9.4). In the nearly completed example shown, the problem is how to get from 67 to 18. Subtraction is an obvious way to do it, but how many should be subtracted? Young children often guess a number such as 40, work out 67 − 40 on the calculator, and use the result, which is 27, to improve the next trial. This is certainly a 'trial and improvement' method, but is less sophisticated than would be expected at Level 5. In fact, the targets on estimation and approximation are unlikely to cause problems to children who work in CAN, but the Statements of Attainment may need to be clarified in order to help teachers to assess them.

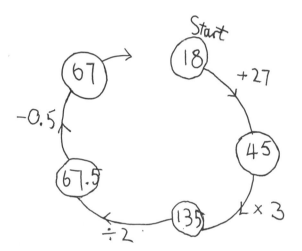

Figure 9.4

Project teachers and children will find the target on number patterns and sequences very attractive. Some Statements of Attainment are:

Explain number patterns and predict subsequent numbers where appropriate. [AT 5, Level 3]

Generalise, mainly in words, patterns which arise in various situations. [AT 5, Level 4]

These targets will enable teachers to exploit the interest in number patterns which forms a major feature of many children's enjoyment of number (see pages 13 and 14). The approach to algebra through number patterns will also build on a topic which children understand and enjoy.

The present and the future

The CAN project has been very fortunate that National Curriculum mathematics is much in line with the thinking that the project has developed. Teachers who work in the project have welcomed the emphasis in the

National Curriculum on a broad curriculum in mathematics, on using and applying mathematics, on the encouragement for children to use their own methods of calculation, and on the possibility of using calculators for much of the work. Teachers in project schools have commented on a number of occasions that they need to make many fewer changes to their curriculum than other teachers.

However, technology continues to develop, as does thinking about mathematics education. It is to be expected that the next few years will bring further developments in the technology of both calculators and computers; mathematics in the primary school will need to develop as the technology changes. How will the National Curriculum need to change when graphic calculators become cheap enough for every primary child to have access to one, in the way that today they can have access to a four-function calculator? What changes will come about in the primary mathematics curriculum, and in other curriculum areas, when every child has daily access to a cheap and portable lap-top computer? Both these developments are, if not just round the corner, at least well over the horizon.

Much of the primary mathematics curriculum is based on the mathematical opportunities which are accessible in the children's environment. Years ago, the environment contained mathematical stimuli based on shops, measuring tools, books, and pencil and paper. Now the environment also contains radio, television, calculators, computers and a variety of specialised mathematical equipment such as apparatus for building solid shapes and structural apparatus for number. Many children are widely travelled and some speak more than one language.

In acknowledging the general suitability of the content of the present National Curriculum in mathematics for the technology and thinking of the early 1990s, we need to be aware that this is not the end of the road. Technology and the environment will continue to develop, and mathematics education will need to move with them. Some of the dangers of too fixed a mathematics curriculum are shown in a quotation from the 1990 Presidential Address to the Mathematical Association by Peter Reynolds, then Mathematics Adviser for Suffolk, and a pioneer in the use of calculators in schools:

In 1984 I attended a European research seminar on primary mathematics where I was able to relate the interesting calculator work that some Suffolk teachers were doing. This caused much interest since none of the other European countries had been allowed to develop the use of calculators because – you guessed it – they had a national curriculum!

The good health of primary mathematics in Britain will only be ensured if National Curriculum mathematics constantly keeps pace with both the technology and the thinking of its time. As a project, CAN was a product of the late 1980s. Changing circumstances will require new developments.

10 | SHOULD YOUR SCHOOL JOIN CAN?

The way of the future

There is no doubt that electronic calculators are here to stay, and their facilities will continue to increase. Most adults and many children now own calculators. People use a calculator because it takes the labour out of calculation, and it is so simple to use. No longer is calculation a tiresome chore, but a brief step in carrying out whatever task a person is engaged in.

The education system will not be able to withstand for ever this change in the technology of calculation. Every child from the age of about six – and some much younger than six – knows that calculators exist. It will inevitably become more and more difficult to persuade children of the need to learn difficult and time-consuming pencil-and-paper methods of calculation when they know that those methods have now been replaced, outside school, by a cheap, portable and easily available machine, to which most of them already have access at home. The resistance to calculators in some schools is an exceptional response to one tool among many modern technological tools; schools find other modern tools acceptable, and make use of them whenever they are useful. Some modern tools which are acceptable in schools are electric cookers and irons, television sets, video players and cameras, computers and ball-point pens.

The headteacher of a school in County Durham in the CAN project wrote about the new technology of calculation in this way:

Calculators are now used almost exclusively, in home, industry and commerce, for all types of calculation. Pocket calculators are cheap, readily available in most homes, and are already being treated as disposable equipment, to be replaced when the batteries run down. They are not going to go away and are likely to become even more sophisticated; for these reasons alone it is essential that children should be taught how to use them sensibly.

Schools must take advantage of the tremendous potential of calculators to remove the chore of number crunching and allow the child time and freedom to investigate numbers, examine problems and develop logical thinking. The CAN philosophy is now a major factor in determining the mathematics policy in primary schools. Unlike ita or the primary French initiatives it is not a temporary phase but a vital development in preparing children for the demands of the 21st century. It is not the initiative of a few 'trendy educationalists' but a logical response to the requirements of the 'real world' in the light of rapid technological progress.

The inevitability of progress in using the new technology of calculation in school does not make CAN an easy step for a school to take at present. Schools are often rightly resistant to change until the teachers are convinced that the change will be for the better. And it is a major change to relinquish the methods of pencil-and-paper calculation which have held sway in schools for 100 years or more. In fact, before calculators were invented, pencil-and-paper methods were the most up-to-date and powerful technology available for calculation; only in the last few years has the position changed.

Although the majority of adults, in their own personal lives, have given up most pencil-and-paper calculation in favour of the calculator, it is still the case that today's adults went through primary schools in the era of pencil-and-paper arithmetic. Indeed, many adults still think that primary mathematics is learning your tables and doing pencil-and-paper arithmetic. The adults who learnt pencil-and-paper methods at school include the parents of all the children in primary schools today. Parents, like teachers, often find it difficult to accept change until they are convinced that the change will be for the better.

Another factor which makes it difficult to change to calculator use in primary schools is that in most published primary mathematics schemes the number work is still based on teaching the traditional vertical pencil-and-paper methods of calculation. Teachers who relinquish this traditional number work have to devise for themselves many of the activities for their children to use.

The National Curriculum in mathematics will be very helpful in increasing calculator use in schools, as it requires children to use all three methods of calculation: mentally, with pencil and paper, and with a calculator. At first, many schools will probably respond to this requirement by adding calculator activities alongside their existing curriculum. Although schools often introduce the use of calculators in this way, this is not CAN. However, Chapter 9 shows how closely compatible are National Curriculum mathematics and the ideas of CAN. The National Curriculum should not prevent any school which wishes to do so from going over to CAN, rather than merely adding calculator use to the existing curriculum.

The need for commitment and support

It is not sensible for one teacher, who only has a class of children for one year, to expect good long-term results from starting on CAN as an individual teacher. Early success may well be achieved; most children quickly become very involved in CAN. Children enjoy the availability of calculators, and make sensible use of them; they also become confident in exploring and investigating mathematics for themselves, and in using their own methods. However, after only one year of CAN, these changes in children's methods and attitudes are unlikely to survive if the next teacher does not continue CAN, but insists that particular methods must be used, or restricts the use of calculators and opportunities for exploration and discovery.

Experience has shown that teachers need much support when they move into CAN, while they realise the need to develop new approaches and teaching styles, and while they attempt to make these changes. An individual teacher who was not able to persuade colleagues to continue with CAN as the children grew older is not likely to find the needed support and sharing of experience among those colleagues. Ideally, as the first group of children move up through the school, CAN should become a whole-school enterprise, in which all the teachers share and support each other.

A key factor in the success of CAN is the headteacher's commitment and support; the headteacher will have to lead the work, to convince members of staff, and to support all the teachers as they make the needed changes. The headteacher will also have to monitor the work within the school, and will have to present the project to parents and governors. The mathematics coordinator also has an important part to play in leading the work, supporting colleagues, devising activities and ensuring the availability of calculators, apparatus and other resources.

A school may be able to find sources of support from outside its own resources. It may be possible for teachers to visit an existing project school before deciding whether to join CAN, or to invite a project teacher to discuss CAN with the staff. The LEA mathematics adviser may be able to provide some support, and to put the school in touch with other schools which are moving in the same direction. Teachers in all the project LEAs have emphasised the importance of teachers' meetings, where ideas and problems could be worked on, and activities devised and shared. If a small school starts to work alone on CAN, only one teacher will probably be involved during the first year. This teacher is likely to feel very isolated if there is no opportunity to meet with other teachers who are doing similar work. A group of schools which start together on CAN can support each other, and may also be able to attract support from an advisory teacher or other outside 'expert'.

Other considerations

As a school decides whether to embark on CAN, several additional factors should be taken into account. The style of mathematics teaching used in the school at present needs to be considered. CAN is likely to be more successful when the school's present practice is child-centred, practical and investigational. On the other hand, if teachers and children are accustomed to following a published mathematics scheme page by page, the changes needed will be greater, and teachers are likely to find them more disturbing. Some project schools had previously made use of published schemes; most of these schools did not immediately abandon the whole scheme, but only replaced the number aspect of the scheme. This meant that the teachers did not at once need to revise all their work in mathematics, but were able to concentrate on developing the number work.

Another factor to be considered is the rate of turnover of both teachers and pupils. If a primary school has a rapid turnover of pupils, the problem of dealing with children who join a project class and find its method of working unfamiliar to them will be greater. A rapid turnover of teachers means that new teachers have to be inducted into CAN at frequent intervals, perhaps at a time when few teachers with experience and expertise about CAN remain in the school to support them.

In some types of school organisation, children who embark on CAN will move to a different school during the primary phase of education; they may move from an infant school to a junior school, or from a first school to a middle school. In these cases, the receiving school needs to be consulted. In CAN, continuity of teaching style and approach are important, and the teachers in the receiving school will need to take part in the project when the children reach them. A receiving school which had not been consulted would have a legitimate cause for complaint when it received a group of children whose experience had been very different from that of their predecessors. Ideally, teachers from the receiving school should be involved in meetings and discussions before the first children reach them. Problems can also arise when a receiving school takes pupils from both project schools and other schools, especially if the children from different schools are accustomed to working in very different ways.

Some thought should also be given to the children's likely progression to secondary schools. However, this is more difficult to tackle in advance, as the children will probably not move to secondary schools until five or more years after the time when a primary school first considers embarking on CAN. In those five years, the personnel and style of teaching in the secondary school mathematics department may change completely. Children from the same primary school also often move to several different secondary schools.

However, the primary school will need to engage in liaison with the secondary schools as the children get near the age of transfer. The need for liaison may cause anxiety to some primary teachers, but differences in attitude between primary and secondary mathematics are becoming smaller, and liaison is becoming easier. Calculators are now acceptable in most secondary schools, and both the National Curriculum in mathematics and GCSE require children to use a calculator, to calculate mentally, and to engage in problem-solving and investigational work. Another link between primary and secondary education is that the National Curriculum Attainment Targets in mathematics provide for a continuous development of children's mathematics from the age of five to 16. On the negative side, some secondary schools still seem to expect children to perform large calculations without a calculator; it is to be hoped that the National Curriculum will make this attitude a thing of the past. In general, the key to successful liaison is the building up of mutual confidence between primary and secondary colleagues, so that ideas and problems in the teaching of mathematics can be shared, and children can progress smoothly to the next phase of education.

As a primary school embarks on CAN, the children's parents and the governing body will need to be informed. Experience shows that, when the parents have confidence in the school, most parents are very supportive of CAN, especially when they begin to see what their children are able to do in mathematics, and how much they are enjoying mathematics. However, some parents do remain unconvinced, and a few take a firm view that CAN is wrong. The use of calculators in the National Curriculum may help to convince this last group. In general, parents cannot be informed about CAN once and for all; the briefing of parents needs to be an on-going enterprise throughout the children's time in the school.

This book has tried to give a balanced picture of the triumphs and difficulties, the problems and the discoveries, the excitements and the anxieties, of the schools which first embarked on CAN, and of the effects of CAN on teachers and children. If a school is considering embarking on CAN, the staff should work together to consider and discuss the range of points made throughout the book, before a decision is made.

Finally, the nine LEAs which were involved in CAN, as Partner or Affiliated LEAs of the PrIME Project, have now banded together to form the **CAN Continuation Project**, to run for the period 1989-92. Page 77 gives a list of the LEAs and schools which took part in CAN during the period 1986-9. In all the LEAs listed, further schools have now joined the project. Several LEAs which were not originally involved have affiliated to the CAN Continuation Project, as some of their schools have moved into CAN. During its life, the CAN Continuation Project will be glad to give any possible support to schools which are beginning to work on CAN.

REFERENCES

DES (1982). *Mathematics Counts: Report of the Committee of Inquiry into the Teaching of Mathematics in Schools* [The Cockcoft Report]. HMSO

DES and Welsh Office (1989). *Mathematics in the National Curriculum*. HMSO

Durham County Council (1989). *CAN in County Durham*

Fitzgerald, A. (1985). *New Technology and Mathematics in Employment*. Department of Curriculum Studies, University of Birmingham

Mathematical Association (1985). *Calculators in 16+ Examinations*

NCC (1989). *Mathematics: Non-Statutory Guidance*. National Curriculum Council

Open University (1982). *PM537 Calculators in the Primary School: A Short Course on the Role of Calculators in Primary Mathematics*

Oram, W.J. (1989). *Some Notes on CAN and the Suffolk County Mathematics Test*. Suffolk County Council

Reynolds, P. (1990). Full circle: 1990 Presidential Address, *Mathematical Gazette*, vol. 74, no 469, October 1990, pp 211–223

Shuard, H. and Smith, D. (1985). Mathematics 6–13: an exploratory study, *SCDC Link*, Summer, p 9

Shuard, H., Walsh, A., Goodwin, J. and Worcester, V. (1990). *Children, Mathematics and Learning*. Simon and Schuster

Straker, A. (1985). Positive steps, *Times Educational Supplement*, 5 April 1990, p 34

This appendix is based on the experience of the CAN project in using calculators in primary classrooms, with children from the age of six upwards.

Physical characteristics of calculators

The first factors which schools need to consider in choosing calculators are sturdiness and price. Sturdiness is vital; children are very heavy-handed, and the calculators will be continuously pounded over a period of years, and will occasionally be dropped on the floor. Another problem about the length of a calculator's life is that the keys of some calculators are constructed in such a way that tiny fingers can pull them from their sockets, so destroying the calculator; it would seem that rubber keys are sometimes prone to this disadvantage. If the battery compartment is accessible to children, they may take out the batteries; indeed, if the calculator uses tiny batteries, they might be swallowed.

An 'automatic power down' feature is an excellent saver of battery life. Children often forget to switch off a calculator, but calculators with an automatic power down feature switch themselves off if no key is pressed for about five minutes.

Some infant teachers prefer large calculators with spaces between the keys. Children with poor motor control may find it easier to press the right key when the keys are not too close together. However, the CAN project has used ordinary pocket calculators with children from the age of six, and the closeness of the keys does not seem to be a difficulty for most children. A clear display is important, but children do not have the difficulty in reading the display that some teachers initially expect.

Calculators which are powered by solar cells do not suffer from battery problems. However, they are more expensive than battery-powered calculators, and if the classroom is very poorly lit, they may not always operate. The length of life of the batteries, and the cost of their replacement, need to be balanced against the greater initial cost of solar calculators. It is sometimes possible to obtain calculators at a reduced price through bulk purchase, perhaps through the LEA's purchasing organisation.

Another factor to be considered is balancing the number of calculators required against the cost of each calculator. In a CAN environment, children should have a calculator available whenever they need it, and should not have to wait for someone else to finish using a calculator. Ideally, a calculator needs to be available for each of the children who are doing mathematics at the same time; sharing should be avoided.

Four-function calculators

The cheapest and simplest calculators available are known as 'four-function' calculators. They are able to carry out addition, subtraction, multiplication and division, and they often have square root and percentage keys and a memory. They can usually display numbers with up to eight digits, and they can handle decimals as well as whole numbers.

Even the simplest four-function calculators are suitable for young children when they start to use calculators. However, some four-function calculators have more features than others, and not all calculators behave in exactly the same way. Less confident teachers often feel happier if all the calculators in the classroom are of the same model and behave in exactly the same way. However, more confident teachers may be able to help children to discover new mathematical insights through comparing the behaviour of different calculators.

All calculators can display negative numbers when they are obtained as answers to calculations; every calculator will show −2 when the keys

$$\boxed{3}\ \boxed{-}\ \boxed{5}\ \boxed{=}$$

are pressed. However, not all four-function calculators allow the user to input −2 directly from the keyboard. To allow the input of negative numbers, a change-sign key (usually labelled +/−) is needed. The input

$$\boxed{2}\ \boxed{+/-}$$

then produces the display −2. The absence of a change-sign key is not a disadvantage at first, but within the first year of CAN, some children discovered negative numbers, and wished to explore them on their calculators. As children grow older, a change-sign key becomes essential.

Another feature of some calculators which young children enjoy exploring is the 'constant function'. On many calculators, the constant function is not controlled by a separate key, and children may not find it for some time. On many calculators, the key sequence

$$\boxed{2}\ \boxed{+}\ \boxed{=}\ \boxed{=}\ \boxed{=}\ \boxed{=}\ \dots$$

produces successive displays of 2, 4, 6, 8, . . . , allowing children to explore the repeated addition of a number. The key sequence

$$\boxed{2}\ \boxed{+}\ \boxed{=}\ \boxed{4}\ \boxed{5}\ \boxed{=}$$

produces the display 47. On some calculators, the + key

needs to be pressed twice to activate the constant function. On other calculators, the constant function works on all four operations $+$, $-$, $\times$, $\div$. On a few calculators, the constant function is controlled by a separate key, usually labelled K.

Four-function calculators usually display eight digits. Any further digits which an answer should contain are lost. For example, the answer to $1 \div 3$ is displayed as

0.3333333

These are the first eight digits of the recurring decimal 0.3333333333.... When 0.3333333 is multiplied by three, the calculator gives the answer as 0.9999999, which may surprise a child who rightly thinks that

$1 \div 3 \times 3 = 1$.

However, the much greater price of a calculator which gives 1 as the answer to $1 \div 3 \times 3$ is probably not worth it for young children.

Most four-function calculators deal with operations strictly in the order in which they are entered. For example, the calculator evaluates

$4 + 5 \times 6$

as 54, working out $4 + 5$ and then multiplying the answer by 6. This is unfortunately contrary to the convention usually used in mathematics. The mathematical convention requires multiplications to be evaluated before additions, so that

$4 + 5 \times 6 = 34$.

However, the mathematically correct answer can be obtained on a four-function calculator by working out $5 \times 6 + 4$ instead of $4 + 5 \times 6$.

Calculators which lose digits after the eighth and which carry out operations in the order in which they are keyed in are said to have 'arithmetic logic'. Most four-function calculators have arithmetic logic. Calculators with arithmetic logic are comparatively cheap to produce, and they contain all the operations which very young children need.

Scientific calculators

The alternative to the arithmetic logic found on four-function calculators is 'algebraic logic'. Scientific calculators, which are usually used in secondary schools, have algebraic logic.

Scientific calculators are more expensive than four-function calculators, but they have many additional features, and the algebraic logic does away with some of the disadvantages of four-function calculators. For example, a scientific calculator usually displays numbers of only eight digits, but the internal calculation is carried out with several more digits (perhaps 11 in all) and the calculator *rounds* its answers to eight digits before displaying them. This avoids the inaccuracy of four-function calculators;

for example, a scientific calculator gives the answer to $1 \div 3 \times 3$ as 1.

Scientific calculators also follow the usual mathematical convention about the order of operations; for example, the key strokes

| 4 | + | 5 | × | 6 | = |

produce the result 34, by storing the addition until the multiplication has been carried out, as is required by the standard mathematical notation. All scientific calculators have a change-sign key, so that negative numbers can be keyed in directly. They correctly evaluate multiplications of negative numbers such as

$-2 \times -3 = 6$

The CAN Continuation Project has found that by the age of nine or ten, some of the more able children are ready to tackle further mathematical challenges with their calculators; some scientific calculators are being introduced to provide new challenges. These calculators will allow the children to explore such mathematical ideas as rounding a decimal to a particular number of decimal places, operations on negative numbers, and the mathematical order in which operations are carried out.

Scientific calculators have other features which are likely to be of interest to many older primary children. Powers of numbers can be evaluated using the x^y key, so that children can explore numbers such as 2^4 and 10^5. Most useful of all, scientific calculators overcome most of the limitations of the eight-digit display. When very large numbers are multiplied on a four-function calculator, the result may overflow the display, and an 'error message' E is displayed. For example, $4\,000\,000 \times 2\,000\,000$ gives an error message. However, on a scientific calculator the result of this calculation is displayed as

8   12

This is the calculator's notation for the very large number 8×10^{12} (or $8 \times 1\,000\,000\,000\,000$, which is 8 followed by 12 zeros). Numbers written in this form, which is known as 'scientific notation', can also be entered directly into the calculator by using the EE key.

Features such as these, which are found on scientific calculators, will give older primary children a rich field for mathematical exploration. It is not yet known whether primary children will explore other mathematical ideas for which scientific calculators provide keys, such as the trigonometric functions. Some scientific calculators also have keys which make statistical calculations easy. The full range of keys on a scientific calculator provide all the functions which students will need up to A-level and beyond.

ACKNOWLEDGEMENTS

The following LEAs worked as Partner LEAs of the PrIME Project, and took part in CAN from 1986 onwards:

Doncaster
Durham/Newcastle upon Tyne consortium
Dyfed (funded by SCDC Wales/CCW)
Suffolk

Without the enthusiasm and commitment of the mathematics advisers in these LEAs, the project could not have taken place. It was a courageous decision in 1985 to allow even a few schools to abandon the traditional pencil-and-paper methods of calculation. The mathematics advisers who have worked with CAN in these LEAs since 1985 are:

Joyce Davies and Graham Haney (Doncaster)
Chris Jones and Trevor Robshaw (Durham)
Colin Noble-Nesbitt (Newcastle upon Tyne)
Peter Moody (Dyfed)
Peter Reynolds and Basil Reid (Suffolk)

Another key group were the coordinators appointed by each LEA. Some have worked in CAN since 1986, others for a shorter period. They ran meetings, visited schools, worked alongside class teachers, explained the project to parents and other teachers, and solved all problems. They are:

Joyce Davies and Graham Galtrey (Doncaster)
Sheila Galbraith (Durham)
Dilys Jones and Sally Francis (Dyfed)
Pauline Smith (Newcastle upon Tyne)
Bernard Bagnall, Monica Adlam and Peter Critchley (Suffolk)

The schools which took part in the project from its beginning in 1986 are listed below. Very grateful thanks are due to the headteachers and staff of these schools for the excellent imaginative work that they contributed to CAN. Without their enthusiasm and continuing hard work there would have been no CAN.

Doncaster
Shaw Wood Infant School, Armthorpe
Shaw Wood Junior School, Armthorpe
Bessacarr First School, Doncaster
Crookesbroom First School, Hatfield
Hexthorpe First School, Shadyside
Richmond Hill First School, Sprotbrough
Richmond Hill Middle School, Sprotbrough

County Durham
Barrington Church of England Primary School, Stanhope,
  Bishop Auckland
Bearpark Primary School, Durham
Heighington Church of England Primary School, Newton Aycliffe
Newker Infant School, Chester-le-Street
Newker Junior School, Chester-le-Street
St Joseph's Roman Catholic Primary School, Durham

Dyfed
Ysgol Y Dderwen, Caerfyrddin
Ysgol Hafodwenog, Trelech
Ysgol Parc-y-Tywyn, Burry Port

Newcastle upon Tyne
Atkinson Road Primary School
Canning Street Primary School
Hotspur Primary School
St Vincent's Roman Catholic Primary School
Stocksfield Avenue Primary School

Suffolk
Sidegate Primary School, Ipswich
Stutton Primary School, Ipswich
Trimley St Martin Primary School, Ipswich
Tudor First School, Sudbury

The names of all the teachers who took part in CAN in these schools are listed on this page and the next. Many of their words are to be found in the anonymous quotations in this book.

In some LEAs, other schools joined the project in later years. These schools are not listed here; however, they have done a great deal of excellent work, and have built with enthusiasm on the work of the pioneering schools.

The project is very grateful for the work of the two evaluators. One of them, Janet Duffin, took on the enormous task of evaluating the work in the 22 schools in England, while Welsh speaker Elaine Thomas evaluated the work taking place in Welsh-medium schools in Dyfed. The insights which the evaluators gained contributed much to the development of the project.

Four other LEAs, which affiliated to PrIME, mounted CAN in some of their schools. They received very little help from the PrIME project, but they succeeded in making CAN work. They have now become full members of the CAN Continuation Project. They are:

Havering
ILEA (Tower Hamlets)
Lancashire
Rochdale

The following seconded teachers and overseas visitors worked with the PrIME project for substantial periods of time, and contributed much to the work:

David Curtis   Paul Donaldson
Wendy Garrard   Kevin Green
Lynda Maple   Veronica Ruth

The project could not have operated without the support of its two excellent administrators Gail Holly and Angie Ashton.

The people listed below contributed to the development of CAN in the five participating LEAs during the period 1986–9. They include the headteachers and many class teachers in the schools, and advisory teachers and mathematics advisers in the five LEAs.

Anne Abbott, Mary Ackroyd, Theresa Adams, Monica Adlam, Carol Agnew, Margaret Alderson, Karen Amory, Eileen Anderson, Margaret Anderson, Shirley Angel, Carol Avers.

Bernard Bagnall, Elizabeth Bailey, Jean Baker, Janet Barrett, Miriam Barron, Pauline Bebbington, Phil Bell, Ted Bendelow, Pauline Bentham, Jane Bradley, Amanda Brand, Linda Bray, Jill Brooks, Bob Bruce, Janet Budd, Elizabeth Burn, Mary Butters.

Karen Cade, Stephanie Caldwell, Eddie Casey, Pam Caunt, Margaret Chapman, Janice Charlton, Linda Charlton, Pat Charlton, Dulcie Child, Anne Clarke, Jenny Clarke, Janine Corkes, Thelma Cowie, Angela Craggs, Peter Critchley, David Crowe, Sister Bernadine Cullen.

Janet Dalton, Norma Dance, Joyce Davies, Tanya Davies, Alison Dawson, Jenny Deary, Yvonne Dickenson, George Dixon, Moira Dixon, Ian Donnelly, Kath Dougan, Janet Duffin, Vivienne Erdos, David Evans, Maureen Fagandini, Leila Farley, Sue Felton, Roger Fern, Kevin Flint, Sally Francis, Sally Frost.

Sheila Galbraith, Pat Gall, Graham Galtrey, Pauline Gardner, Jill Garrett, Wendy Garrard, Karen Garton, Joan Gibson, Adele Goddard, Audrey Graham, Lyn Gray, Joan Gregg, Jan Griffiths.

Beryl Hall, Graham Haney, Sheila Harrup, Tom Hedley, Alison Herbert, Alec Herring, Sue Hewlett, Val Hichen, David Hill, David Hill, Madeline Hill, Linda Hoste, Katie Howson, Val Hudson, Sally Hulme, Michael Hunter, Elaine Hutchings, Rhiannon Ifan.

Berwyn Jenkins, Anne Johansen, Dilys Jones, Chris Jones, Gerwyn Jones, Lynette Jones, Rhuddwen Jones, Susan Kanfinan, Sylvia Kearley, Ann Knowles, Anne Lamb, Cath Lawson, Jean Leese, Eileen Lister, Debbie Litchfield, Jane Lockwood, Maureen Lowen, David Loy, Vince Lynch.

Neil Macleod, Pauline Magee, Claire Martin, Maria Louisa Massagli, Sister Josepha Matthews, Meg Matteer, Val Mawhinney, Gustar Mcleod, Judith Merrill, Peter Milner, Clive Minnican, Elizabeth Mold, Peter Moody, Mike Moor, Ann Moore, Neil Moore, Francine Moralle, David Morgan.

Meryl Norval, Colin Noble-Nesbitt, Keith Oglesby, Bill Oram, Elaine Parkin, Janet Parsons, Graham Pearson, Margaret Peart, Ed Penfold, Eileen Perrin, Tim Plant, Maureen Portcous, Pat Porter, Annette Prendergast.

Janet Rees, Basil Reid, Gillian Reynolds, Peter Reynolds, Joan Richards, Penry Richards, Kathy Richardson, Lesley Ritchie, Angela Robertson, Gill Robinson, Trevor Robshaw, Jane Roscoe, Laurie Rousham, Sally Rutter.

Diane Sawyer, Howard Schofield, Dorothy Scott, Mike Scott, Dorothy Smith, Pauline Smith, Sheila Smith, Shelagh Smith, Janet Stainforth, Vida Stanton, W Stockdale.

Lois Taylor, Marjorie Taylor, Maureen Taylor, John Thirlwell, Elaine Thomas, Karoline Thomas, Moira Thomas, Wendy Thomas, Dorothy Thompson, June Treherne, Joy Urwin, Carol Ventom.

Helen Walker, Carol Walton, Elizabeth Wandless, Amanda Warren, Terri Watson, Pat Webb, Margaret Weedon, Brenda Whilton, Donna Williams, Jean Williams, Ann Williamson, Debbie Woods, Ruth Young.

Copyright materials

INDEX